ANIMALS
STICKER-PEDIA

Silver Dolphin

San Diego, California

Silver Dolphin

Silver Dolphin Books
An imprint of the Advantage Publishers Group
5880 Oberlin Drive, San Diego, CA 92121-4794
www.silverdolphinbooks.com

Author: Jinny Johnson

Copyright © Marshall Editions, 2003

A Marshall Edition
Conceived, edited, and designed by Marshall Editions
The Old Brewery, 6 Blundell Street, London N7 9BH, U.K.
www.quarto.com

ISBN-13: 978-1-59223-555-1
ISBN-10: 1-59223-555-7

1 2 3 4 5 09 08 07 06 05

Originated in Singapore by Universal Graphics
Printed and bound in China by CT Printing
Design: Roger Christian and Ivo Marloh
Cover design: Ivo Marloh
Copyediting: Andrew Mackay

The Access Code for your CD-ROM is:
TIGER

Contents

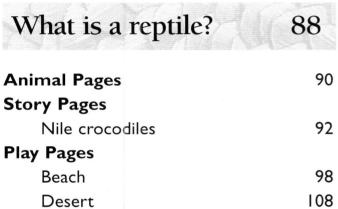

How to use this book

This Sticker-pedia has four parts. In the first part we introduce you to mammals, the second part is about birds, the third is reptiles, and the last part is all about amphibians.

On the Animal Pages you can add the stickers that are found at the back of this book. You can also read some fascinating facts about each animal.

In the Story Pages you can find out more about some of your favorite animals, such as tigers and elephants.

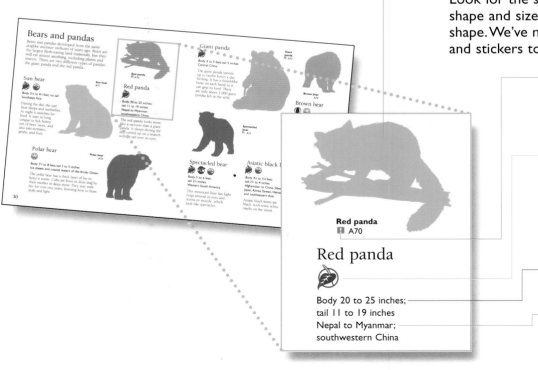

Sticker shape
This is where you put your stickers. Look for the sticker that matches the shape and size of the colored animal shape. We've numbered all the animals and stickers to help you match them up.

Extinction warning!
This symbol tells you that the animal is in danger of dying out.

Habitat
These symbols show you what sort of environment this animal lives in. The symbols are explained on the next page.

Size
The length of the animal.

Range
The regions in which this animal is found.

Red panda

Body 20 to 25 inches; tail 11 to 19 inches
Nepal to Myanmar; southwestern China

You can have even more sticker fun with the Play Pages. Try arranging your stickers in the different landscapes.

You'll find all your stickers at the back of the book. The ones for the Animal Pages are on pages 129 to 154. The stickers for the Play Pages are on pages 155 to 160. Start sticking!

Pond play page
You can find all the stickers of amphibians that live by lakes and ponds on page 160. Stick them on this page to create your own pond scene.

Key to habitat symbols

Temperate grassland
Open country in areas with a mild climate: steppe, prairie, bush, moors, and lowlands

Tropical grassland
Open country in areas with a hot climate: savanna

Northern forest
Forests in cold, northern regions: taiga, boreal, and coniferous forests

Deciduous forest and seasonal forest
Forests in areas with a mild or tropical climate

Tropical evergreen forest
Forests in hot regions: rain forests and mangroves

Desert
Desertlike areas in hot regions: rocky areas, sandy areas, semidesert, scrub, brushland, and very dry land

Inhabited areas and agricultural land
Areas close to where people live: gardens, orchards, parks, farmland, towns and cities, hedgerows, and roadsides

High ground
Areas located high above sea level: hills, volcanoes, and mountains

Tundra and polar
Icy regions: the Antarctic and Arctic Circles

Freshwater
Inland water: rivers, lakes, ponds, lagoons, streams, wetlands, marshes, swamps, floodplains, springs, ditches, dams, riverbanks, and underground water in caves

Coast
Land bordering the sea: mud flats, shores, cliffs, islands, and tidal areas

Coastal water
Seawater close to land: estuaries and the seabed

What is a mammal?

All mammals are warm-blooded, have lungs to breathe in air, and a bony frame called a skeleton. Most have large brains, good senses, and are covered with hair or fur.

Indian elephant

Mammals are warm-blooded. This means that they can keep their body at the same temperature all the time. Many mammals sweat to cool down.

Senses

Most mammals have good senses of sight, hearing, smell, taste, and touch. These senses help them find food and avoid enemies.

Types of mammals

Most mammals give birth to live young. The babies of marsupials, a type of mammal, are very small at birth and crawl into a special pouch, where they can grow stronger in safety. Monotreme mammals are unusual, as they lay eggs instead of having live babies.

MONOTREME
Short-nosed echidna

Female has a shallow egg pouch on her belly.

Echidnas have no nipples—milk oozes from pores in their skin.

MARSUPIAL
Baby wallaby feeding in pouch

MARSUPIAL
Ring-tailed wallaby

Powerful legs for bounding along fast

Long, thick tail for balance

Good hearing

Sharp eyes

Keen sense of smell

Sensitive whiskers

8

Suckling

Instead of having to gather food for her babies like other animals, a female mammal is able to make her own food. She produces milk, which the babies suck from nipples. The milk contains all the food that the babies need to grow and stay healthy.

Female wild boar with young

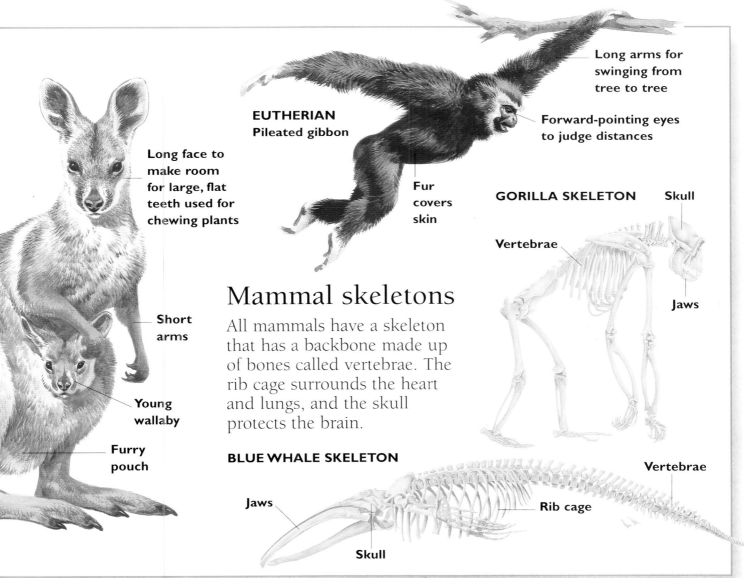

Long face to make room for large, flat teeth used for chewing plants

Short arms

Young wallaby

Furry pouch

EUTHERIAN
Pileated gibbon

Long arms for swinging from tree to tree

Forward-pointing eyes to judge distances

Fur covers skin

GORILLA SKELETON

Skull

Vertebrae

Jaws

Mammal skeletons

All mammals have a skeleton that has a backbone made up of bones called vertebrae. The rib cage surrounds the heart and lungs, and the skull protects the brain.

BLUE WHALE SKELETON

Jaws

Skull

Rib cage

Vertebrae

9

Monotremes and marsupials

With most mammals, the babies grow inside their mother's body for a long time before they are born. But monotremes and marsupials are different. Just like reptiles, monotremes lay eggs. When the eggs hatch, the young feed on their mother's milk like other mammal babies. When baby marsupials are born, they are very small. Some are no bigger than a grain of rice, and all are hairless and blind. Young marsupials live in a furry pouch on the underside of their mother's body, feeding on milk until they are big enough to leave the pouch.

Long-nosed echidna
⚠ A1

Long-nosed echidna

**Body 17¾ to 30¾ inches; virtually no tail
New Guinea**

Echidnas have long, slender snouts, no teeth, and weak jaws. They grab insects with their rough tongues.

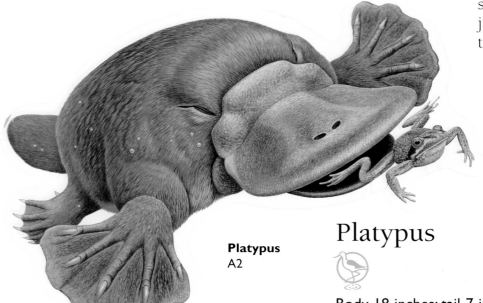

**Platypus
A2**

Platypus

**Body 18 inches; tail 7 inches
Australia**

The platypus spends the day in its riverside burrow. At dawn and dusk it comes out to feed on insects, worms, grubs, crayfish, and frogs.

Short-nosed echidna

Body 13¾ to 19¾ inches; tail 3½ inches
Australia; southeastern New Guinea

The echidna's spines protect it from enemies. When attacked, it curls into a ball or digs into soil so that only its spines are showing. This protects its face and underparts.

**Short-nosed echidna
A3**

**Kowari
A4**

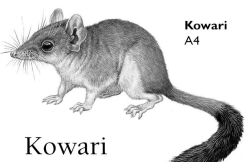

Kowari

Body 6½ to 7 inches;
tail 5 to 5½ inches
Central Australia

Kowaris live alone or in small groups in a burrow. At night, they hunt for insects, lizards, and birds. They breed in winter and have five or six young at a time.

**Water opossum
A5**

Water opossum

Body 10½ to 13 inches;
tail 14¼ to 15¾ inches
Central and South America

The water opossum is the only marsupial that lives in water. It swims with its webbed hind feet and feeds on fish, shellfish, and other small water creatures.

Virginia opossum

Body 12¾ to 19¾ inches;
tail 10 to 21 inches
North and Central America

**Virginia opossum
A6**

This is the only marsupial native to North America. It often feeds around dumps and garbage cans. To escape its enemies, the opossum may "play dead," lying on its side with its tongue hanging out and its eyes shut.

Koala

Body 23¼ to 33½ inches;
virtually no tail
Eastern Australia

The koala spends up to 18 hours each day sleeping. It spends the rest of its time feeding on the leaves of eucalyptus trees.

Koala
A7

Wombat

Body 27¼ to 47 inches;
virtually no tail
Eastern Australia; Tasmania

The wombat lives in forests and scrubland. It feeds on grass and can go without water for months at a time. In summer, it shelters from the heat in a burrow.

Wombat
A9

Tasmanian devil

Body 20¼ to 31¼ inches;
tail 9 to 11¼ inches
Tasmania

The slow-moving Tasmanian devil is about the size of a small dog. It has a good sense of smell and feeds on reptiles, birds, fish, and small mammals.

Tasmanian devil
A10

Brush-tailed opossum

Body 12½ to 22½ inches;
tail 9½ to 13¼ inches
Australia; introduced into New Zealand

The brush-tailed opossum lives in woodland and feeds on flowers, fruit, and insects.

Short-nosed bandicoot

Body 11½ to 13 inches;
tail 3 to 7 inches
Southeastern Australia; Tasmania

The short-nosed bandicoot finds its food, mainly worms and insects, by smell.

Short-nosed bandicoot
A11

Red kangaroo

Body 3 to 5 feet; tail 35 to 43 inches
Central Australia

The red kangaroo lives in the desert and is the largest marsupial. It bounds along on its long back legs, reaching speeds of up to 35 miles an hour. A baby kangaroo, which lives in its mother's pouch, is called a joey.

Red kangaroo
A12

Bridled nail-tail wallaby

Body 17½ to 26 inches;
tail 13 to 26 inches
Eastern Australia

The nail-tail gets its name from a small, fingerlike nail hidden in thick hair at the tip of its tail. It eats grass and roots.

Bridled nail-tail wallaby
⚠ A15

Musky rat-kangaroo
A14

Musky rat-kangaroo

Body 9 to 13½ inches;
tail 5 to 6½ inches
Northeastern Australia

Unlike other kangaroos, the musky rat-kangaroo moves around on all fours like a rabbit. It usually gives birth to twin babies.

Greater glider
A13

Greater glider

Body 11¼ to 19 inches;
tail 17½ to 21½ inches
Eastern Australia

The greater glider has flaps of skin between its wrists and ankles. It glides from tree to tree in the eucalyptus forests where it lives.

Lumholtz tree kangaroo

Lumholtz tree kangaroo
A16

Body 20½ to 31½ inches; tail 16½ to 36½ inches
Australia

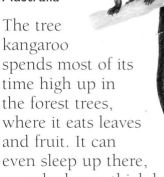 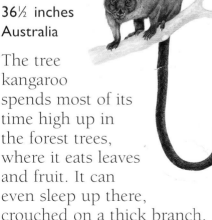

The tree kangaroo spends most of its time high up in the forest trees, where it eats leaves and fruit. It can even sleep up there, crouched on a thick branch.

Anteaters, armadillos, pangolins, aardvarks, and sloths

Anteaters are toothless mammals, but armadillos have up to a hundred small teeth. These mammals do not need big teeth because they feed on ants and termites, which they lick up with their tongues. Sloths feed on leaves, chewing them very slowly. Pangolins and aardvarks have lifestyles similar to armadillos and anteaters, but are not closely related to them.

Three-toed sloth
A17

Three-toed sloth

Body 19¾ to 23½ inches;
tail 2½ to 2¾ inches
Northern South America

This is the slowest mammal, reaching a top speed of just seven feet per minute.

Giant anteater
A18

Giant anteater

Body 3¼ to 4 feet;
tail 25½ to 35½ inches
Central and South America
to northern Argentina

This anteater sniffs out ant nests and termite mounds and breaks them open with its claws. It then licks up the insects with its long, sticky tongue.

Giant armadillo

Body 29½ to 39½ inches;
tail 19½ inches
South America, from Venezuela
to northern Argentina

The giant armadillo's body is covered with horny plates. It weighs up to 132 pounds and is very strong. It breaks open ant nests and termite mounds with its front legs.

Giant armadillo
 A19

14

Nine-banded armadillo
A20

Nine-banded armadillo

Body 17¾ to 19¾ inches;
tail 9¾ to 15¾ inches
Southern U.S.; Central and South America

This armadillo spends most of the day asleep in a burrow. When attacked, it rolls itself up into a ball.

Aardvark

Body 3¼ to 5¼ feet; tail 17½ to 23½ inches
Africa, south of the Sahara

The aardvark has a kangaroo-like tail, piglike body, and rabbitlike ears. It feeds on termites at night. During the day, the aardvark sleeps in a burrow, which it digs with its strong feet.

Aardvark
A21

Giant pangolin
A22

Northern tamandua

Body 21¼ to 22¼ inches;
tail 16 to 26 inches
From southern Mexico to northern South America

The tamandua is an anteater that lives in trees. It is a good climber, using its tail for gripping. A baby tamandua travels around the forest on its mother's back.

Northern tamandua
A23

Giant pangolin

Body 29½ to 31½ inches;
tail 19¾ to 25½ inches
Eastern and central Africa

The giant pangolin's body is covered with large scales. When feeding on ant nests, thick eyelids protect its eyes from bites. It can roll up into a ball if threatened, or lash out with its tail, which is covered in razor-sharp scales.

Moles, tenrecs, shrews, hedgehogs, colugos, and solenodons

Moles, tenrecs, shrews, and hedgehogs feed on insects and small creatures such as worms, centipedes, snails, and spiders. Many of these mammals have long, narrow snouts for searching out food, and sharp teeth and claws. Most have poor sight but a good sense of smell.

Streaked tenrec
A24

Streaked tenrec

Body 6¼ to 7½ inches; no tail
Madagascar

The streaked tenrec has a coat of spines to protect it from enemies.

European hedgehog

Body 5 to 10 inches; tail ⅓ to 2 inches
Europe; introduced into New Zealand

European hedgehog
A25

The hedgehog makes piglike grunts as it moves around the undergrowth looking for small creatures to eat. If it is attacked, the hedgehog curls up into a ball.

Giant golden mole
A26

Star-nosed mole

Body 4½ to 5 inches; tail 3 to 3½ inches
Southeastern Canada; northeastern U.S.

The star-nosed mole feeds on worms, insects, and fish, which it finds on the bottoms of ponds and streams.

Star-nosed mole
A27

Giant golden mole

Body 7¾ to 9½ inches; no tail
South Africa

The giant golden mole hunts on the ground for beetles, lizards, slugs, and worms.

Colugo

Body 15 to 16½ inches; tail 8¾ to 10½ inches
Philippines

Also known as the flying lemur, a colugo has flaps of skin between its neck and tail, allowing it to glide up to 440 feet.

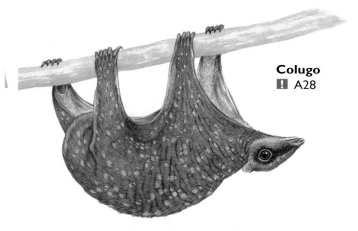

Colugo
⚠ A28

Common tree shrew
A29

Common tree shrew

Body 5½ to 9 inches; tail 4¾ to 8¼ inches
Southern Asia

This squirrel-like creature is an excellent climber. It feeds on ants, spiders, seeds, buds, small birds, and mice.

Short-eared elephant shrew

Body 3 to 5 inches; tail 3 inches
Southern Africa

Elephant shrews have long, trunklike noses. They can hop like small kangaroos.

Short-eared elephant shrew
⚠ A30

Cuban solenodon

Body 11 to 12½ inches;
tail 6¾ to 9¾ inches
Cuba

The solenodon has a poisonous bite for killing lizards, frogs, and birds.

Cuban solenodon
⚠ A31

Armored shrew
A32

Armored shrew

Body 4¾ to 6 inches;
tail 2¾ to 3¾ inches
Central Africa

The armored shrew lives in forests. It feeds on insects and other small creatures.

17

Bats

Bats are the only true flying mammals. They fly through the air on smooth wings of skin, making sudden turns and twists. Most bats spend the day asleep, hanging upside down. At night, they launch themselves into the air to hunt for food. Some bats find their food by making high-pitched sounds that bounce, or echo, off nearby objects and are picked up by the bat's ears.

Linnaeus' false vampire bat
A33

Spear-nosed bat

Body 4 to 5¼ inches; tail 1 inch; wingspan 17¼ to 18½ inches
Central America and northern South America

The spear-nosed bat eats mice, birds, and small bats, but will also eat insects and fruit. In turn, it is hunted by false vampire bats. It lives in buildings and caves. At dusk, the flock leaves to fly to their feeding grounds. The female gives birth to a single baby once or twice a year.

Spear-nosed bat
A34

Linnaeus' false vampire bat

Body 5 to 5¼ inches; no tail; wingspan 30 to 39 inches
Southern Mexico to Peru and Brazil; Trinidad

This is the largest bat in North and South America. It does not drink blood like a true vampire bat.

Ghost bat

Body 4½ to 5½ inches; no tail; wingspan 15¾ to 23½ inches
Northern and western Australia

The ghost bat gets its name from the eerie color of its pale fur at night. It lives in many different places, from forests to deserts, and feeds on mice, birds, geckos, and other bats.

Ghost bat
⚠ A35

Greater fruit bat
A36

Greater fruit bat

Body 13¾ to 15¾ inches;
no tail; wingspan 5 feet
Southern and southeastern Asia

The greater fruit bat has the
largest wings of any bat in
the world. It feeds on fruit
and nectar.

Tube-nosed fruit bat

Body 2¾ to 4¾ inches;
tail ½ to 1 inch; wingspan
7¾ to 11 inches
Pacific islands near New Guinea

This bat has strange,
tube-shaped nostrils,
which stick out on
each side of its head.
They probably help
it to find ripe fruit
such as guavas, figs,
and coconuts.

**Tube-nosed
fruit bat**
A37

Greater horseshoe bat

Body 4¼ to 5 inches;
tail 1 to 1½ inches;
wingspan 13 inches
Europe; Asia; northern Africa

This bat feeds on beetles,
swooping down to snatch
them off the ground.
It roosts in caves,
trees, and the roofs
of old buildings.

**Greater
horseshoe
bat**
A38

American long-eared bat

Body 1½ to 2 inches; tail 1¼ to
1¾ inches; wingspan 9 to 11 inches
Southwestern Canada; U.S.; Mexico

This bat has very long ears, which it
uses to hear insects. The long-eared
bat feeds at night, mainly on moths.
During the day, it roosts in
buildings and trees.

**American
long-eared bat**
A39

Primates

Humans, monkeys, apes, lorises, tarsiers, and lemurs all belong to a group of mammals called primates. These mammals have large brains, making them intelligent and quick to learn new skills. Many primates have thumbs that can move across their palms to press against their fingers, allowing them to grasp objects firmly. Most primates live in trees, and they have forward-pointing eyes to help them judge distance.

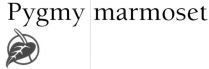

**Pygmy marmoset
A40**

Pygmy marmoset

Body 5½ to 6¼ inches;
tail 6 to 7¾ inches
South America: upper reaches of Amazon River area

This is one of the smallest primates. It is often attacked by large birds, so it tries to keep out of sight.

**Ring-tailed lemur
⚠ A41**

Slender loris

Body 7 to 10¼ inches;
virtually no tail
Southern India; Sri Lanka

This primate grips branches tightly as it swings through the trees. It creeps up on its prey quietly.

**Golden lion tamarin
⚠ A43**

Golden lion tamarin

Body 7½ to 8¾ inches;
tail 10¼ to 13½ inches
Southeastern Brazil

This beautiful primate gets its name from the silky, lionlike mane that covers its head and shoulders. It lives in family groups in trees.

Ring-tailed lemur

Body 17¾ inches; tail 21¾ inches
Madagascar

The ring-tailed lemur climbs to the tops of trees to sunbathe after a cold night. Male lemurs produce a scent, which they use to mark their territory.

**Slender loris
⚠ A42**

Greater bush baby

Body 10½ to 18½ inches;
tail 13 to 20½ inches
Central and southern Africa

The bush baby gets its name from its call, which sounds like a baby crying. It hunts at night, using its large eyes to see its prey. It pounces and kills its victims with just one bite.

Greater bush baby
A44

Western tarsier

Body 14¼ to 17¼ inches;
tail 19¾ to 23½ inches
Madagascar

The tarsier hunts at night and has huge eyes to see its prey in the dark. Its eyes are so big that they cannot move from side to side. Instead, the tarsier can turn its head all the way around. It also has large, batlike ears to hear the sounds of its small prey.

Western tarsier
A45

Emperor tamarin

Body 7 to 8¼ inches;
tail 9¾ to 12½ inches
Western Brazil; Peru; Bolivia

The emperor tamarin has a long, drooping "mustache." Small troops of tamarins dart through the trees looking for insects, fruit, leaves, and flowers to eat. They will also steal bird eggs.

Emperor tamarin
A46

Aye-aye

Body 3¼ to 6¼ inches;
tail 5¼ to 10½ inches
Sumatra and Borneo

Aye-aye
A47

The aye-aye taps on trees with its long middle finger, then listens for insects moving under the bark. It then uses the same finger to pull the insects out.

Woolly spider monkey

Body 24 inches;
tail about 26¼ inches
Southeastern Brazil

This monkey moves around the rain forest by using its long arms and tail to swing from branch to branch. It is becoming rarer because the rain forest is being cut down.

Woolly spider monkey
⚠ A48

Red howler

Body 31½ to 35½ inches;
tail 31½ to 35½ inches
South America

Red howler monkeys live in the rain forest in groups of as many as 30. They are very noisy, and their howling can be heard up to three miles away.

Red howler
A49

Monk saki
A50

Monk saki

Body 13¼ to 19 inches;
tail 12¼ to 20 inches
South America

The monk saki has long, shaggy hair around its face, and a thick, bushy tail. It lives high in the trees and never comes down to the ground. It can make huge leaps between branches.

White-fronted capuchin
A51

White-fronted capuchin

Body 11¾ to 15 inches;
tail 15 to 19¾ inches
South America

This monkey lives in trees. It is always picking things up, hoping to find something to eat. It feeds on a wide variety of plants and small creatures.

Diana monkey

Body 15¾ to 22½ inches;
tail 19¾ to 29½ inches
Western Africa

This colorful monkey is a very good climber, and spends almost all its time high up in the trees of the rain forest. Groups of up to 30 monkeys live together, led by an older male. They feed mainly on plants, but also eat insects and the eggs and young of birds.

Diana monkey
⚠ A52

Mandrill
A53

Mandrill

Body 21¾ to 37½ inches;
tail 2¾ to 4 inches
Western central Africa

The mandrill has a bright red nose and blue cheeks. The female gives birth to a single baby, which she carries around with her, either on her back or clinging to her belly. Mandrills live in forests and feed on fruit, nuts, worms, and mushrooms.

Japanese macaque

Body 19¾ to 29½ inches;
tail 2½ to 4½ inches
Japan

Macaque monkeys live in forests in Japan's mountains. In cold winters, these monkeys keep warm by bathing in volcanic springs, where water heated deep below ground comes to the surface to form steaming pools.

Japanese macaque
⚠ A54

Proboscis monkey

Body 20¾ to 30 inches;
tail 21¾ to 30 inches
Borneo

The male proboscis monkey
has a very long nose,
which turns red
when he is excited.
Proboscis monkeys live
in swamps and jungles.

**Proboscis
monkey**
❗ A55

Red colobus

Body 18 to 27½ inches;
tail 16½ to 31½ inches
Western, central, and
eastern Africa

This monkey lives in large
troops of up to 100 animals.
The troop contains many
family groups. The red
colobus makes big
leaps between the
branches of trees as
it searches for food.

**Red
colobus**
A56

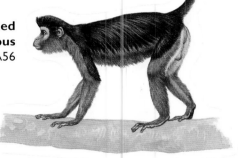

Olive baboon

Body up to 3¼
feet; tail 17¾ to
29½ inches
Western, central,
and eastern Africa

Olive baboons live in troops of up to 150
animals, eating leaves, seeds, roots, bark,
fruit, insects, eggs, and lizards. They spend a
lot of time grooming each other's fur.

Olive baboon
A57

Allen's swamp monkey

Body 15¾ to 19¾ inches;
tail 17¾ to 21¾ inches
Congo and Democratic
Republic of Congo

This rare monkey lives near rivers and
in swamps. It mostly eats leaves and
fruit, but also goes into the water to
catch crabs and even fish.

**Allen's
swamp
monkey**
A58

24

Orangutan

Height 4 to 5 feet; no tail
Borneo and Sumatra

The orangutan is the second largest primate. It builds a tree nest out of sticks, in which it sleeps. A female orangutan gives birth to a single baby.

Orangutan
A59

Chimpanzee

Body 25¼ to 37 inches; height 4 to 5½ feet; no tail
Western, central, and eastern Africa

The chimpanzee mainly eats plants, but sometimes also insects and meat. It uses objects such as stones and sticks as simple tools.

Chimpanzee
A60

Lar gibbon

Body 16½ to 22¾ inches; no tail
Southeast Asia

The lar gibbon lives in trees and rarely comes down to the ground. It swings through the trees and runs along branches. It lives in small family groups.

Lar gibbon
A61

Gorilla

Height 4½ to 6 feet; no tail
Western central Africa

Gorillas spend most of their time on the ground. They feed on plants. Young gorillas travel on their mother's back until they are two or three years old.

Gorilla
⚠ A62

Savanna play page

You can find all the stickers of mammals that live in tropical grasslands on page 155. Stick them on this page to create your own savanna scene.

Dogs

All domestic dogs are descended from wolves. Wolves and other wild dogs have long legs for chasing prey, and sharp teeth for killing it. A dog's sense of smell is very important—it uses its nose to find food and recognize other animals. Wild dogs hunt animals as small as mice and as large as moose. Some wild dogs, such as foxes, live on their own, but others, such as wolves and hunting dogs, live and hunt in groups called packs.

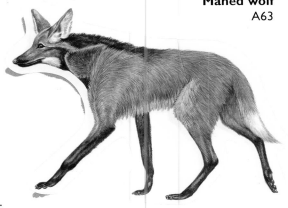

Maned wolf
A63

African hunting dog

3 to 4 feet long
Africa

Hunting dogs hunt as a pack, chasing a group of animals such as wildebeest. They try to separate one victim from the herd, then move in for the kill.

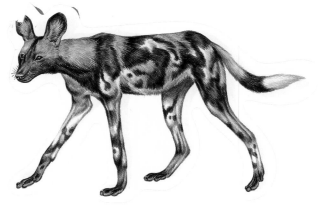

African hunting dog
⚠ A64

Maned wolf

4 feet long
South America

The maned wolf is similar to a red fox, but has longer legs and a longer muzzle. It is wary of humans and hunts mainly at night. It eats small animals, birds, and plants.

Bush dog

2 to 3 feet long
South America

The bush dog looks more like a small bear than a dog. It may claim another animal's den to sleep in.

Bush dog
⚠ A65

Arctic fox

1 to 2 feet long
Northern Europe; Asia;
North America

The arctic fox's fur turns white in winter to hide it against snow. When the snow melts, its fur turns brown again to blend in with rocks and plants.

Arctic fox
A66

Fennec fox

1 to 2 feet long
Northern Africa;
southwestern Asia

The fennec is the smallest fox. Its large ears allow heat to escape from its body, so it stays cool in the hot deserts where it lives.

Fennec fox
A67

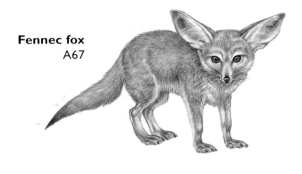

Red fox
A68

Red fox

1 to 3 feet long
North America; Europe;
Africa; Asia

Red foxes live and hunt alone and only come together to breed and rear their young. They usually hunt rodents, rabbits, and other small animals.

Gray wolf
A69

Gray wolf

3 to 4 feet long
North America; Eastern
Europe; Asia

This is the largest of all the wild dogs. Gray wolves live in packs that hunt over an area of nearly 400 square miles. They howl loudly to warn others to stay away.

29

Bears and pandas

Bears and pandas developed from the same doglike ancestor millions of years ago. Bears are the largest flesh-eating land mammals, but they will eat almost anything, including plants and insects. There are two different types of pandas: the giant panda and the red panda.

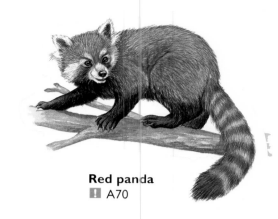

Red panda
A70

Sun bear

Body 3½ to 4½ feet; no tail
Southeast Asia

During the day, the sun bear sleeps and sunbathes. At night it searches for food. It uses its long tongue to lick honey out of bees' nests, and also eats termites, grubs, and fruit.

Sun bear
A71

Red panda

Body 20 to 25 inches; tail 11 to 19 inches
Nepal to Myanmar; southwestern China

The red panda looks more like a raccoon than a giant panda. It sleeps during the day, curled up on a branch with its tail over its eyes.

Polar bear

Body 7¼ to 8 feet; tail 3 to 5 inches
Ice sheets and coastal waters of the Arctic Ocean

The polar bear has a thick layer of fur to keep it warm. Cubs are born in dens dug by their mother in deep snow. They stay with her for over two years, learning how to hunt seals and fight.

Polar bear
A72

Giant panda

Body 4 to 5 feet; tail 5 inches
Central China

The giant panda spends up to twelve hours a day feeding. It has a thumblike bone on each hand so it can grip its food. There are only about 1,000 giant pandas left in the wild.

Giant panda
■ A73

Brown bear
A74

Brown bear

Body 5 to 8 feet; small tail
Europe; Asia; North America

This bear is also known as the grizzly bear. It eats leaves, berries, fruit, nuts, and roots, and sometimes insects, rodents, fish, and even large mammals.

Spectacled bear
■ A75

Spectacled bear

Body 5 to 6 feet;
tail 2¾ inches
Western South America

This mountain bear has light rings around its eyes and across its muzzle, which look like spectacles.

Asiatic black bear

Body 4¼ to 5¼ feet;
tail 2¾ to 4 inches
Afghanistan to China, Siberia, Japan, Korea, Taiwan, Hainan, and southeastern Asia

Asiatic black bears are black, with some white marks on the snout.

Asiatic black bear
A76

31

Raccoons and mustelids

Like bears, raccoons evolved from doglike ancestors. Raccoons are long-tailed, meat-eating mammals that spend much of their time in trees. Mustelids are small or medium-sized meat-eaters with a long body, short legs, and a long tail. Some mustelids live in the sea, while others live on land, either burrowing or climbing.

Coati

Body 17 to 26¼ inches; tail 17 to 26¾ inches
Southeastern U.S.; Central and South America

With its long nose, the coati searches in holes and cracks in the ground for insects, spiders, and other small animals. Coatis hunt both day and night.

Raccoon
⚠ A77

Coati
A78

Kinkajou
A79

Kinkajou

Body 16 to 22½ inches; tail 15¾ to 22 inches
Eastern Mexico through Central and South America to Brazil

The kinkajou lives in trees and is a good climber. It uses its tail to grip the branches, leaving its hands free to pick food. It feeds at night, mainly on fruit and insects.

Raccoon

Body 16¼ to 23½ inches; tail 7¾ to 15¾ inches
Southern Canada; U.S.; Central America

The raccoon runs and climbs well and can also swim. It is most active at night. As well as catching prey such as frogs, fish, mice, and birds, it often raids garbage cans in search of food.

Wolverine

Body 25½ to 33¾ inches; tail 6¾ to 10¼ inches
Siberia; Scandinavia; North America

The wolverine is a very strong animal and can kill prey larger than itself. It spends most of its life on the ground, but it will climb trees to find bird eggs.

Wolverine
A80

Grison

Body 18½ to 21½
inches; tail 6 inches
Southern Mexico to
Peru and Brazil

The grison is good at climbing
and swimming. It feeds on frogs,
worms, and other ground-living
creatures. It uses another
animal's old burrow
or a hole in a rock or
tree stump as a den.

Grison
A81

American badger

Body 20 to 28 inches;
tail 4 to 6 inches
Southwestern Canada
to Mexico

The badger lives in a burrow
underground, which it digs
with its strong claws. It
comes out at dusk to hunt
for prey such as rodents,
birds, and snakes.

**American
badger
A82**

Sea otter

Body 3¼ to 4 feet;
tail 9¾ to 14¼ inches
Bering Sea; California

This otter feeds on
shellfish and uses rocks
to help it open the hard
shells. It lies on its
back in the water and
bangs its prey against
a rock.

**Sea otter
A83**

Striped skunk

Body 11 to 15 inches; tail 7 to 9¾ inches
North America

Skunks are well known
for the strong smell they
make when threatened.
The smell makes it
difficult for an enemy
to breathe and
hurts its eyes.

**Striped skunk
A84**

33

Civets and mongooses

Civets are tree dwellers that hunt for prey at night. Their coats are generally spotted or striped. Mongooses are fast-moving ground dwellers and live in Africa and Asia. Their long bodies are ideal for chasing prey such as insects and small animals.

Ermine

Body 9 to 11 inches;
tail 3¼ to 4¾ inches
Europe; Asia; North America

The ermine hunts rodents and rabbits and kills them with a bite to the back of the neck. It also eats birds, fish, and insects. In northern parts of the world, its fur turns white in winter.

Meerkat

Body 9½ to 11¾ inches;
tail 7½ to 9½ inches
Southern Africa

Meerkats are a type of mongoose. Several families may live together as a group. While most of the group looks for food such as insects, birds, and fruit, some keep watch for danger.

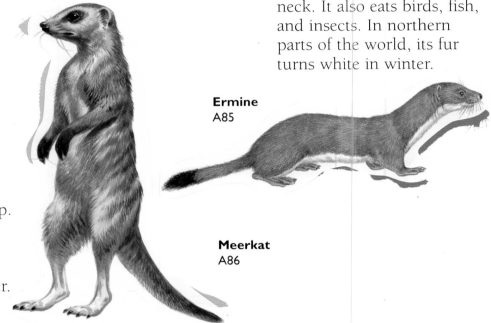

Ermine
A85

Meerkat
A86

African palm civet
A87

African palm civet

Body 17 to 23½ inches; tail 19 to 24½ inches
Central Africa

This civet has short legs and a long, thick tail. It climbs well and spends much of its life in trees, where it rests during the day. At night it feeds on insects and small animals.

Indian mongoose
A88

Banded linsang

Body 14¾ to 17 inches; tail 12 to 14 inches
Thailand; Malaysia; Sumatra; Borneo

The banded linsang varies from whitish-gray to brownish-gray in color, with four or five dark bands across its back and dark spots on its sides and legs. It is nocturnal and spends much of its life in trees. It eats birds, small mammals, insects, lizards, and frogs.

Indian mongoose

Body 13¾ inches; tail 9¾ inches
Iraq to Southeast Asia; introduced
into the West Indies, Hawaii, and Fiji

The mongoose eats almost any food it can catch, including snakes, scorpions, and insects. It is popular among humans because it hunts pests such as rats and mice. As a result, the mongoose has been introduced into several new countries.

Banded linsang
A89

Fossa

Body 23½ to 29½ inches;
tail 21½ to 27½ inches
Madagascar

The fossa is the largest meat-eating mammal in Madagascar, and it resembles a cat. It has a long tail and a reddish-brown coat. It is mainly active at dusk and at night. It lives in trees and hunts mammals, birds, lizards, snakes, and insects.

Fossa
A90

Cats and hyenas

Cats hunt other animals. They have strong legs for chasing prey and pouncing. A cat's claws are drawn back into its toes when walking or running. When they pounce, the claws come out and grip their prey. Most cats have coats patterned with spots or stripes.

Striped hyena

Body 3¼ to 4 feet; tail 9¾ to 13¾ inches
Northern and eastern Africa through southwestern Asia to India

Hyenas look more like dogs, but are actually related to cats. They feed mainly on dead animals, but also hunt small mammals, birds, lizards, snakes, and insects.

Striped hyena A92

Mountain lion

Body 3¼ to 5¼ feet;
tail 23½ to 33½ inches
Western North America;
Central and South America

Deer are the main prey of this hunter. Having stalked its victim, it pounces and kills it with a swift bite to the neck.

Mountain lion A93

Lynx A91

Lynx

Body 31½ to 39 inches;
tail 1½ to 3¼ inches
Northern North America

The lynx has good eyesight and spots mice 250 feet away. The tufts on its ears help it hear in forests, where sound does not travel well.

Wild cat

Body 19¾ to 25½ inches;
tail 9¾ to 15 inches
Europe; Africa; southwestern Asia; India

The wild cat looks like a domestic cat, but is larger. It is a good tree-climber. In courtship, males howl and screech to attract a mate.

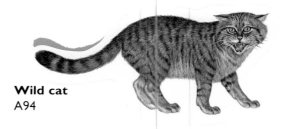

Wild cat A94

36

Leopard

Body 4¼ to 6¼ feet;
tail 3½ to 4½ feet
Africa, south of the Sahara;
southwestern and southern Asia

The leopard drags the bodies of large prey up into trees, out of reach of hyenas and jackals. Its coat has spots to hide it among the leaves of the trees and grass.

Leopard
A95

Snow leopard

Body 4 to 5 feet; tail 3 feet
Central Asia

The snow leopard feeds mainly on wild sheep and goats. Its broad, furry feet keep it from sinking in snow.

Snow
leopard
⚠ A96

Lion

Male **Female**

Body 4½ to 6½ feet;
tail 26¼ to 39½ inches
Africa, south of the Sahara;
northwestern India

Female lions do most of the hunting, often stalking antelopes and zebras in pairs or larger groups. The males' role is to defend the group's territory and babies.

Lion
⚠ A97

Cheetah

Body 3½ to 4½ feet;
tail 25½ to 31½ inches
Africa, south of the Sahara;
southwestern to central Asia

The cheetah is the fastest land mammal, and can go from zero to 60 miles an hour in just three seconds. It mainly hunts antelopes.

Jaguar

Body 5 to 6 feet;
tail 27½ to 36 inches
Southern U.S.; Central and South America

The jaguar is a good swimmer and hunts fish as well as land animals. It also climbs trees, where it may lie in wait for prey.

Jaguar
A98

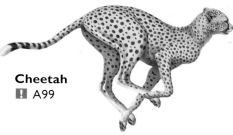

Cheetah
⚠ A99

37

Siberian tiger

Caspian tiger

Indo-Chinese tiger

Sumatran tiger

Tigers

The tiger is the biggest of all the wild cats. In the last hundred years, tigers have become very rare due to hunting and the cutting down of forests. There are now just 5,000 to 7,000 wild tigers left. They live mainly in parts of India, Southeast Asia, and Siberia. Tigers live alone, roaring to tell other tigers to keep away from their territory. They hunt large mammals, usually at night, and may travel up to twelve miles in search of food. Tigers usually try to avoid people.

Tiger types

Tigers vary in size and color, depending on where they live. Animals from northern areas, such as Siberia, are larger and paler than those from southern tropical areas such as Sumatra. The largest of all is the Siberian tiger. All tigers are now very rare.

Hunting

At dusk, tigers set out to hunt buffalo, deer, wild pigs, and other animals. Their striped coats hide them against the trees and grass as they sneak up on their prey. When they are close enough, they pounce on their victim.

Tiger cubs

Tigers have two to six cubs, which can be born at any time of the year. They stay with their mother for up to three years, learning to hunt.

Unlike domestic cats, tigers like to be near water and take a dip to cool off on a hot day. They are good swimmers and may cross rivers or swim between islands in search of their prey. Tigers can occasionally be seen climbing trees.

Grassland play page

You can find all the stickers of mammals that live on steppes and prairies around the world on page 156. Stick them on this page to create your own wild grassland scene.

Pigs, peccaries, and hippopotamuses

Pigs, peccaries, and hippos are hoofed mammals. They have four toes on their feet, but peccaries have only three on their hind feet. They mostly feed on plants, but some also eat small animals and insects. A pig has a long snout that ends in a round, flat disk. The peccary lives only in the Americas, while the hippo, a larger cousin of pigs and peccaries, is found in Africa.

Wild boar A100

Warthog

Body 3½ to 4½ feet;
tail 13¾ to 19¾ inches
Central and southern Africa

With its lumpy head and curved tusks, the warthog is not a pretty sight. It lives in small family groups on the African savanna and feeds on short grasses and herbs.

Warthog A101

Wild boar

Body 3½ to 4¼ feet;
tail 6 to 7¾ inches
Southern and central Europe; northern Africa; Asia

The wild boar is the ancestor of the barnyard pig. It roots around the forest floor for plants and insects to eat. Young boars have striped coats that camouflage them from enemies.

Hippopotamus

Body 9¼ to 14 feet; tail 13¾ to 19¾ inches
Africa, south of the Sahara

The hippo is one of the world's largest land mammals—only the rhino and the elephant are heavier. It lives near rivers and lakes and spends up to 16 hours each day in the water. It feeds on riverside plants and fruit.

Hippopotamus A102

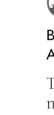
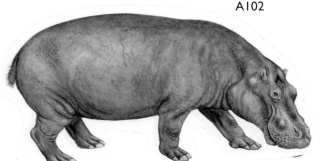

Collared peccary

Body 29½ to 35½ inches;
tail ½ to 1¼ inches
Southwestern U.S.;
Central and South America

Collared peccaries live in groups of up to 15 animals. They eat roots, grass, fruit, worms, and insects. They run fast to escape from enemies such as jaguars and mountain lions.

Collared peccary
A103

Pygmy hippopotamus
🚹 A104

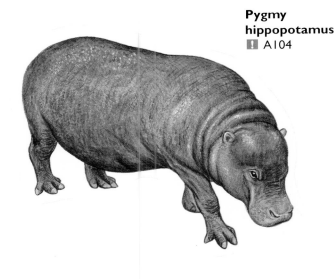

Pygmy hippopotamus

Body 5½ to 6¼ feet; tail 6 to 8¼ inches
Western Africa, from Guinea to Nigeria

This small hippopotamus lives around swamps, but spends most of its time on dry land. The pygmy hippo is becoming rarer because its forest habitat is being cut down. It is also at risk from hunters.

Bearded pig

Body 5¼ to 6 feet; tail 7¾ to 11¾ inches
Malaysia; Sumatra; Borneo

This pig has a long body and a narrow head. It gets its name from the whiskers on its face. It lives in rain forests, scrubland, and swamps, and eats fruit, rats, and insects. The females have two or three piglets.

Bearded pig
A105

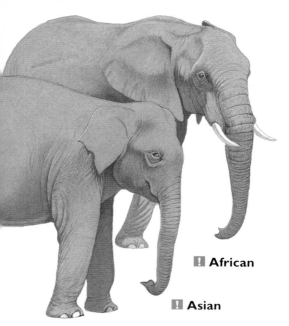

African

Asian

Elephants

The elephant is the largest land mammal. It weighs as much as 13,000 pounds, stands up to 13 feet tall at the shoulder, and can live as long as 78 years. Elephants have a long nose, called a trunk, and a pair of strong tusks.

Two species

There are two species of elephant. The African elephant is larger than the Asian, and has bigger, more rounded ears.

Big appetite

An African elephant spends three-quarters of its time feeding. It eats about 330 pounds of grass, leaves, twigs, and roots every day.

Elephants at work

For thousands of years, humans have trained elephants to lift, push, and drag heavy objects.

A baby elephant does not need to look for food because it drinks its mother's milk for at least two years. Sometimes other adult females in the herd also suckle it.

Showers and mud baths

Elephants keep cool by sucking up water with their trunks and spraying it over their bodies. They also wallow in mud or throw dust over themselves to protect their skin against insects and the sun.

Camels, chevrotain, and musk deer

Camels are hoofed, cud-chewing animals. This means that, when they eat, they briefly chew their food before swallowing it. They then bring the food back into their mouth and chew it again. Chevrotain look like small deer, but are probably related to camels and pigs. Musk deer produce a strong, musky smell.

Arabian camel
A106

Water chevrotain

Body 29½ to 33½ inches;
tail 4 to 6 inches
Western and central Africa

The tiny water chevrotain
is about the size of a small dog.
It lives in forests near water and spends the day resting in undergrowth. If danger threatens, it dives into the water to escape.

Water chevrotain
A107

Arabian camel

Body 7¼ to 11 feet;
tail 19¾ inches
Northern Africa; southwestern Asia; introduced into Australia

Arabian, or dromedary, camels live in the desert. They can go for a long time without food or water.

Vicuña

Body 4½ to 5¼ feet; tail 6 inches
Peru to northern Chile

Vicuñas are humpless camels. They live in small family herds in the mountains of South America, where they feed on grass and small plants. Each herd is guarded by a male. He warns the herd of danger by whistling.

Vicuña
A108

Guanaco
A109

Guanaco

Body 4 to 5½ feet; tail 9¾ inches
Peru to Patagonia

The guanaco is a slim, long-legged animal. It can run very fast and leap up mountain trails. It feeds on grass and lives in small herds in the open country.

Bactrian camel

Body 9¾ feet; tail 20¾ inches
Central Asia: China, Mongolia

The bactrian, or two-humped camel, has been domesticated, but still lives only in the Gobi Desert. This camel has long, shaggy hair, which keeps it warm in winter. The hair is shed in summer, leaving the animal almost naked.

Bactrian camel
⚠ A110

Forest musk deer
A111

Forest musk deer

Body about 3¼ feet; tail 1½ to 2 inches
Himalayas to central China

The male musk deer produces a strong-smelling liquid called musk, which it uses to send signals to females. It feeds on lichens, buds, shoots, grass, moss, and twigs.

47

Giraffes, pronghorns, and deer

These hoofed mammals all chew the cud. Giraffes and pronghorns have horns on their heads, but deer have antlers. The difference is that antlers drop off and grow again each year, but horns do not fall off. Despite their strange appearance, giraffes are actually related to deer. The giraffe is the tallest animal living on land.

Giraffe
A112

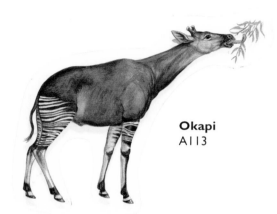

Okapi
A113

Giraffe

Body 10 to 13 feet;
tail 35½ to 43½ inches
Africa, south of the Sahara

The giraffe lives on Africa's savanna. With its amazingly long legs and neck, it stands over 19 feet tall. Its great height allows it to feed on leaves and buds at the tops of trees and to spot approaching danger.

Okapi

Body 4 to 6½ feet;
tail 11¾ to 16½ inches
Democratic Republic of the Congo

The African okapi feeds on the leaves and shoots of rain forest trees. It pulls them off the branches with its long tongue. It lives alone and only meets other okapis during the breeding season.

Pronghorn

Body 3¼ to 5 feet;
tail 3 to 4 inches
Central Canada;
western U.S.; Mexico

The pronghorn can run as fast as 40 miles per hour and is one of North America's fastest mammals. The males have short prongs on their horns.

Pronghorn
A114

48

Moose

Body 8 to 10 feet;
tail 2 to 4¾ inches
Northern Europe; Asia;
North America

The moose is the largest deer.
It has big antlers, a broad
muzzle, and a flap of skin
that dangles from its throat.
It eats shrubs, pinecones, and
water plants and can
swim well.

Moose
A115

Caribou

Body 4 to 7¼ feet;
tail 4 to 8¼ inches
Greenland; northern Europe;
Asia; North America

The caribou is also known
as the reindeer. It is the
only kind of deer in
which both males and
females have antlers.

Caribou
A117

Wapiti

Body 5¼ to 8 feet;
tail 4¾ to 9¾ inches
North America; northern Africa;
Europe; Asia; introduced into
New Zealand

Male and female wapiti live
in separate herds. In spring,
males lose their antlers and
grow new ones. Males take
part in antler-clashing fights.

Wapiti
A116

Pampas deer

Body 3½ to 4¼ feet;
tail 4 to 6 inches
South America, south
of the Amazon

This deer lives among
pampas grass, but
much of its habitat
has been disturbed by
farming. It rests during
the day and feeds on
plants at dusk.

**Pampas
deer**
A118

49

Bovids

Bovids are hoofed plant-eaters. Cows, sheep, and goats are the best-known members of the family. Bovids live in many different habitats around the world and range in size from the rhebok to the giant buffalo. All bovids have a stomach that is split into four parts, and "chew the cud." This means that they bring up food from their first stomach and chew it again.

European bison

Body 7 to 11½ feet;
tail 19¾ to 23½ inches
Eastern Europe

The European bison feeds on leaves, ferns, twigs, bark, and acorns. In 1919 it died out in the wild, but six were bred in captivity and their offspring were released into the wild.

European bison
⚠ A119

Rhebok
A120

Lechwe
A121

Rhebok

Body 3¼ to 4 feet;
tail 4 to 7¾ inches
South Africa; Lesotho; Swaziland

The rhebok is a small antelope with a soft, woolly coat. It lives on grassy hills and high plains with low bushes and few trees.

Lechwe

Body 4¼ to 5½ feet;
tail 11¾ to 17¾ inches
Southern Africa

The lechwe lives around lakes and swamps. It spends much of its time wading in shallow water, where it feeds on grasses and water plants. It has long, wide hoofs, which help it to walk through mud.

Arabian oryx
⚠ A122

Arabian oryx

Body 5¼ feet;
tail 17¾ inches
Saudi Arabia

The oryx lives in the desert and can go for a long time without water. It gets all the water it needs from the grass and other plants it eats. It uses its hoofs and horns to scrape out a hollow under a bush, where it hides from the sun.

Addax

Body 4¼ feet;
tail 9¾ to 13¾ inches
Northern Africa

The addax is one of the few large animals that live in the Sahara. It feeds on desert plants. Its wide hoofs keep its feet from sinking into the sand. It is now very rare because of hunting.

Addax
⚠ A123

Impala
A124

Impala

Body 4 to 5¼ feet; tail 11¾ to 17¾ inches
Southern Africa

The impala has long, spiral-shaped horns. It is at home in woodland or on the African savanna. When running, it can make leaps of up to 33 feet in order to escape enemies, and sometimes does this while playing.

51

Gerenuk
A125

Saiga

Body 4 to 5½ feet;
tail 3 to 4 inches
Central Asia

The saiga lives on high,
grassy plains called steppes.
Its nose has special hairs to
remove dust from the air. They may also help
warm the air it breathes. In winter it grows a
thick coat to protect it from icy winds.

Saiga
⚠ A126

Gerenuk

Body 4½ to 5¼ feet;
tail 9 to 13¾ inches
Africa: Somalia and Ethiopia to
Kenya and Tanzania

This large gazelle has a very
long neck and long legs. The
male has horns and is larger
than the female. Gerenuks
live almost entirely on leaves
and young shoots of thorny
bushes and trees.

Wild yak
⚠ A127

Wild yak

Body up to 10½ feet;
tail 19¾ to 31½ inches
Central Asia

Despite its large size, the yak moves easily
around the remote mountain slopes where
it lives. Its long, thick, ragged hair reaches
almost to the ground. It also has a woolly
undercoat to keep it warm.

Chamois

Body 35½ to 51 inches;
tail 1¼ to 1½ inches
Europe to southwestern Asia

In summer the chamois grazes on mountaintops, often leaping between rocky crags. It has sturdy legs, and hoofs with special pads underneath to help grip slippery surfaces.

**Chamois
A128**

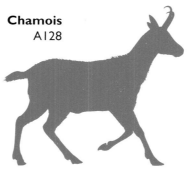

Asian water buffalo

Body 8¼ to 10 feet; tail 2 to 3 feet
India; Southeast Asia

When not feeding, water buffalo spend much of their time wallowing in mud, or underwater with only their muzzles and horns showing. They use their long, curved horns to defend themselves against tigers.

**Asian water buffalo
A130**

**Blue wildebeest
A129**

Blue wildebeest

Body 5½ to 7¾ feet; tail 2 to 3 feet
Southern and eastern Africa

This wildebeest is a large, cowlike antelope. In the dry season, huge herds walk long distances across the African savanna in search of fresh grass and watering holes.

**Bongo
A131**

Bongo

Body 5½ to 8¼ feet; tail 17¾ to 25½ inches
Central Africa

The shy, forest-dwelling bongo hides among the bushes and trees during the daytime. When it runs, the bongo ducks its head to keep its horns from catching on branches.

Horses, rhinos, tapir, and hyrax

Despite their very different appearances, all of these mammals are hoofed plant-eaters. Horses are well adapted for fast, graceful running. In the wild, they live in herds and feed mainly on grass. Tapirs are active at night and usually live in forests. The huge rhinos have one or two horns on their heads and very tough skin with only a few hairs. Hyrax look like rabbits and are tree-climbers.

Grevy's zebra
A132

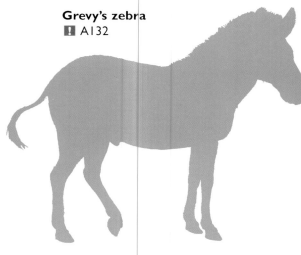

Grevy's zebra

Body 8½ feet;
tail 27½ to 29½ inches
Eastern Africa

This zebra has narrower stripes than other zebras. It lives in dry regions and travels in search of water.

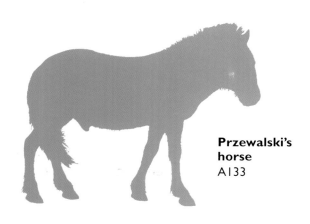

Przewalski's horse
A133

Przewalski's horse

Body 6 feet; tail 35½ inches
Native to Mongolia and western China, but now found only in captivity

This short, sturdy horse is the only true wild horse living today. It now lives only in captivity.

African ass

Body about 4 feet;
tail about 16 inches
Northeastern Africa

This ass is now rare in the wild because of hunting. It spends much of the day resting in shade. It is most active at night.

African ass
A134

Black rhinoceros

Body 9¾ to 11¾ feet;
tail 23½ to 27½ inches
Africa: Chad and Sudan
to South Africa

The black rhino is actually
gray. Its color depends on
the mud in which it
wallows. It has a large head
with two or three horns.

Malayan tapir
A135

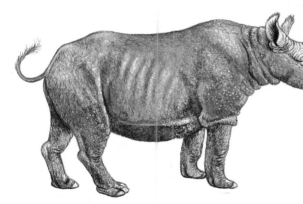

Black rhinoceros
A13f

Malayan tapir

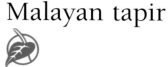

Body 8¼ feet; tail 2 to 4 inches
Southeast Asia: Myanmar to
Malaysia, and Sumatra

The Malayan tapir is a shy
animal and is active only at
night. It has a long trunk.
It swims well and heads for
water if it is alarmed.

Tree hyrax

Body 15¾ to 23½ inches; no tail
Africa: Kenya to South Africa

The tree hyrax is a very good
tree-climber. It lives in a hole
in a tree or a rock crevice,
where it rests during the day.
Tree hyraxes normally live
in pairs and are very noisy;
they make a wide range of
screams, squeals, and grunts.

Indian rhinoceros
A137

Indian rhinoceros

Body 13¾ feet; tail 29½ inches
Nepal; Northeast India

This the largest rhinoceros in
Asia. It has a thick, dark gray skin,
which has lots of small lumps on it.
It has just one horn on its head.

Tree hyrax
A138

55

Meadow play page

You can find all the stickers of mammals that live in woodland or fields on page 156. Stick them on this page to create your own meadow scene.

Rabbits, hares, and pikas

Rabbits, hares, and pikas are all plant-eating mammals. They have sharp front teeth for chewing plant food. Pikas are smaller than rabbits and have short, rounded ears and no tail. Most of the fast-moving rabbits and hares have long narrow ears, small, fluffy tails, and well-developed back legs for jumping.

European rabbit

Body 14¼ to 18 inches; tail 1½ to 2¾ inches
Europe; northwestern Africa; introduced into Australia, New Zealand, and Chile

European rabbits live together in a group of burrows called a warren. There may be up to two hundred rabbits in a colony. They mainly feed on grass and leafy plants, but they also eat grain and can damage trees.

European rabbit
A140

American pika

Body 7¾ to 9¾ inches
Southwestern Canada; western U.S.

Pikas live in family groups that make dens among rocks. Grass and juicy plant stems are their main food. Pikas store up food for the winter.

American pika
A139

Snowshoe hare

Body 14¼ to 20½ inches;
tail 1 to 2 inches
Northern U.S.; Canada; Alaska

This hare's dark brown fur turns white in winter to match the snow. Only the tips of its ears remain dark.

Snowshoe hare
A141

Squirrels, springhares, beavers, and relatives

These animals are all rodents. The squirrel family includes animals such as woodchucks, prairie dogs, and chipmunks. The springhare can leap like a kangaroo. Pocket gophers and pocket mice live in the Americas. Beavers spend much of their lives in water.

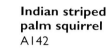

Indian striped palm squirrel
A142

Indian striped palm squirrel

Body 4½ to 7 inches;
tail 4½ to 7 inches
India; Sri Lanka

These squirrels leap about in palm trees, feeding on palm nuts, flowers, and buds.

Woodchuck

Body 17¾ to 24 inches;
tail 7 to 9¾ inches
North America

The woodchuck, or groundhog, eats plenty of plant food in summer. It sleeps through the winter, living on its body fat.

Woodchuck
A143

Gray squirrel

Body 8 to 10 inches;
tail 8 to 10 inches
Eastern U.S.; Canada;
introduced into Great Britain and South Africa

The gray squirrel lives in parks, gardens, and forests. It feeds on acorns and nuts.

Gray squirrel
A145

Black-tailed prairie dog
A144

Black-tailed prairie dog

Body 11 to 13 inches;
tail 3 to 4 inches
Central U.S.; Canada

Prairie dogs live in burrows called towns, which may house thousands of animals.

Plains pocket gopher
A146

Plains pocket gopher

Body 7 to 9½ inches;
tail 4 to 5 inches
Central U.S.

This gopher is called "pocket" because of its cheek pouches. It crams them full of food to carry back to its nest.

Eastern chipmunk
A147

Eastern chipmunk

Body 5¼ to 7¾ inches;
tail 3 to 4½ inches
Eastern North America

The lively chipmunk lives in burrows. It comes out in the morning to forage for food.

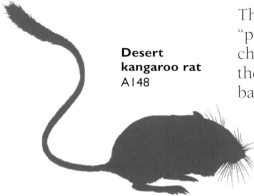

Desert kangaroo rat
A148

Desert kangaroo rat

Body 4¼ to 6½ inches;
tail 7 to 7¾ inches
Southwestern U.S.

The kangaroo rat gets moisture from its food—it may live its whole life without drinking water.

Springhare

Body 13¾ to 17 inches;
tail 14¼ to 18½ inches
Southern Africa

The springhare bounces along on its long hind legs like a kangaroo.

Springhare
⚠ A150

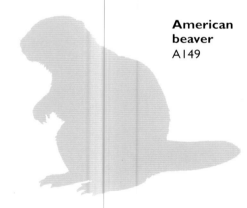

American beaver
A149

American beaver

Body 23 to 31 inches;
tail 7¾ to 12 inches
North America

Beavers are well known for building dams across streams to make ponds.

60

Rats, mice, hamsters, gerbils, and lemmings

All of these animals are rodents. Most eat plants, but some also eat fish and insects. Rodents are found in many different places, from under the ground to near rivers and lakes. Some rodents, like the brown rat, carry diseases, and are considered to be pests by humans.

Deer mouse
A151

Arizona cotton rat
■ A152

Deer mouse

Body 4¾ to 7 inches; tail 3¼ to 7 inches
Canada to Mexico

Like the animal they are named after, deer mice run and hop through grass and forests. They build nests underground or in holes in trees. Deer mice breed for the first time when they are only seven weeks old. They may have several litters a year.

Common hamster

Body 8¾ to 11¾ inches; tail 1¼ to 2¼ inches
From western Europe across central Asia

In late summer the hamster gathers food to store for the winter. During the winter it sleeps, waking up from time to time to feed.

Common hamster
A153

Arizona cotton rat

Body 5 to 7¾ inches; tail 3 to 5 inches
Southwestern U.S.; western Mexico

Cotton rats are sometimes found in large numbers, and can be pests. They feed on plants and small insects but may also take the eggs and chicks of bobwhite quails and eat crayfish and crabs.

Bamboo rat

Body 14¼ to 19 inches; tail 4 to 6 inches
Southeast Asia

This rat has a heavy body, short legs, and a short, almost hairless tail. Its front teeth are large and strong, and it uses these and its claws for digging its underground burrow.

Bamboo rat
A155

Swamp rat
A156

Swamp rat

Body 5 to 7¾ inches;
tail 2 to 6¾ inches
Southern Africa

This rat feeds on seeds, berries, plant shoots, and grasses. It will dive into water to escape enemies— many larger creatures feed on swamp rats.

62

Naked mole rat
A154

Naked mole rat

Body 3¼ to 3½ inches;
tail 1½ inches
Eastern Africa

This little rodent lives in groups of up to 30 animals ruled by a female, or queen. Worker mole rats gather food for the colony to eat.

Norway lemming

Body 5 to 6 inches; tail ¾ inch
Scandinavia

The Norway lemming is busy around the clock, feeding on grass, leaves, and moss. In winter it clears pathways under the snow so it can forage for food. It starts to breed in spring, while still under the snow.

Norway lemming
A157

Great gerbil

Body 6¼ to 7¾ inches;
tail 5 to 6¼ inches
Central Asia

This desert animal lives in the Gobi, a desert with hot summers and icy winters. During the summer, it stores 130 pounds or more of plant material in its burrow so that it has plenty of food for the winter.

Great gerbil
A159

Meadow vole

Meadow vole
A158

Body 3½ to 5 inches; tail 1¼ to 2½ inches
North America

The meadow vole moves around in the grass along runways that it clears and keeps trimmed. It makes a nest on the ground or in a burrow.

Wood mouse

Body 3¼ to 5 inches;
tail 2¾ to 3¾ inches
Europe; Asia

The wood mouse is one of Europe's most common small rodents. It lives in a nest under the roots of trees and hunts for food in the evenings.

Wood mouse
A161

Brown rat
A160

Brown rat

Body 9¾ to 11¾ inches;
tail 9¾ to 12½ inches
Worldwide

The brown rat lives wherever there are people. It has followed humans all over the world and is a pest in many places.

Dormice, jerboas, and porcupines

Although they look very different from each other, these mammals are all rodents. Dormice sleep though the winter. This is called hibernating. During this time they live on their body fat, but wake up from time to time to feed on stored food. Jerboas have long back legs, which are used for jumping. Porcupines have long, sharp spines covering parts of their body and tail.

Desert dormouse

Body 2¾ to 3¼ inches;
tail 2¾ to 3¾ inches
Kazakhstan

This dormouse is active at night. It feeds on plants during the summer and hibernates in a burrow in winter.

Desert dormouse
⚠ A162

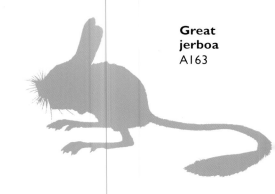

Gundi

Body 6¼ to 7¾ inches; tail ½ to ¾ inch
Africa: Sahara

Gundis are shy animals and are active only at night. They feed on plants, which they eat in the safety of a rock crevice. Gundi babies are able to run as soon as they are born.

Great jerboa

Body 6¼ to 10 inches;
tail 6¼ to 8¾ inches
Central Asia

This lively rodent leaps through the desert on its long back legs. At night it searches for seeds and insects by combing through the sand with the long claws on its front feet.

Great jerboa
A163

Gundi
A164

Tree porcupine

Body 11¾ to 24 inches;
tail 13 to 17¾ inches
Bolivia; Brazil; Venezuela

The body of the tree porcupine is covered with short, thick spines. It uses its tail like an extra leg to grip branches. Tree porcupines usually feed at night on leaves, plant stems, and fruit.

Crested porcupine

Body 28 to 33 inches;
tail up to 1 inch
Africa

The spines on the back of the crested porcupine are up to 12 inches long. If threatened, the porcupine charges backward so that the sharp spines stick into its enemy's body. This porcupine lives in a burrow during the day and comes out at night to feed.

Crested porcupine
A165

Tree porcupine
A166

Meadow jumping mouse
A167

Fat dormouse

Body 6 to 7 inches;
tail 5¼ to 6¼ inches
Europe; Asia

The fat dormouse has a long, bushy tail. It is the largest of its family. It hibernates in a nest in a hollow tree or in an old rabbit burrow.

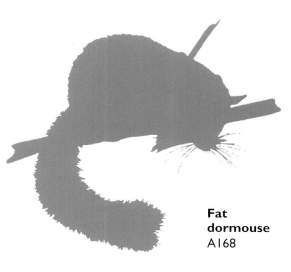

Fat dormouse
A168

Meadow jumping mouse

Body 2¾ to 3¼ inches;
tail 4 to 6 inches
Canada; northern U.S.

Meadow jumping mice bound along in a series of short jumps. They make nests of grass or leaves on the ground. They hunt for food at night.

65

Chinchillas, guinea pigs, capybaras, and tuco-tucos

These animals all belong to small families of medium- to large-sized rodents. All of them live in South America. Some dig burrows, while others shelter among rocks.

Capybara
A170

Capybara

Body 3¼ to 4¼ feet; no tail
Panama to eastern Argentina

The largest living rodent, the capybara spends much of its time in water. It has partly webbed feet, which help it swim and dive.

Chinchilla
⚠ A171

Chinchilla

Body 8¾ to 15 inches;
tail 3 to 6 inches
Northern Chile

The chinchilla has thick fur, which keeps it warm in the mountains where it lives. Chinchillas sit up to eat, holding their food in their front paws.

Guinea pig
A169

Guinea pig

Body 7¾ to 15¾ inches; no tail
Peru to Argentina

Also known as the cavy, the wild guinea pig is not related to pigs, although it squeals like one when excited.

Hutia

Body 11¾ to 19¾ inches;
tail 6 to 11¾ inches
Bahamas

The hutia lives in a burrow, but is a good climber and searches for food in trees.

Hutia
A172

Paca
A173

Paca

Body 23½ to 31 inches; tail 1 inch
Southern Mexico to Suriname,
south to Paraguay

The paca lives alone and is active at night. It spends the daytime in a burrow, which it digs in a riverbank, among tree roots, or under rocks, coming out after dark to feed. It is a good swimmer.

Tuco-tuco

Body 6¾ to 9¾ inches;
tail 2¼ to 4¼ inches
Eastern Argentina

Tuco-tucos look very much like pocket gophers. They have very large front teeth, which are used to loosen the soil when burrowing. Tuco-tucos spend most of their lives underground.

Tuco-tuco
A174

Plains viscacha
A175

Plains viscacha

Body 18½ to 26 inches;
tail 6 to 7¾ inches
Argentina

The plains viscacha has a large head and blunt snout. Males are larger than females. They live in colonies in burrows with many tunnels and entrances.

Mara

Body 27¼ to 29½ inches;
tail 1¾ inches
Argentina

The mara has long legs and feet, which allow it to run and bound along at speeds of up to 18 miles per hour, like a hare or jackrabbit. Maras are active in the daytime and feed on plants. They dig burrows or claim one from another animal.

Mara
A176

Scrubland play page

You can find all the stickers of mammals that live in dry scrubland or desert on page 157. Stick them on this page to create your own desert scene.

What is a bird?

Birds have a strong but light body, two legs, and a pair of wings. All birds are covered with feathers—and they are the only creatures that have feathers. Most birds have good eyesight.

Not all birds fly. The world's largest bird, the ostrich, is too heavy to take to the air. Instead it runs fast on its long legs.

Wings

A bird's wings are shaped for different kinds of flight. Hawks and vultures soar on broad wings. The albatross glides on long wings. Swifts and swallows have long, pointed wings for fast flight. A pheasant's wings are for slow, flapping flight.

Albatross

Swift

Swallow

Hawk

Vulture

Pheasant

Bird anatomy

Here is a martial eagle about to snatch its prey. Strong wings keep its body in the air, and its tail feathers are spread to help it steer during flight. Talons are held ready to crush its prey. Its unlucky victim will be torn apart by the eagle's hooked beak.

Primary flight feathers

Secondary flight feathers

Beak

Talons/claws

All types of feet

Birds have between two and four toes on their feet. Water birds have webbed feet to help them swim.

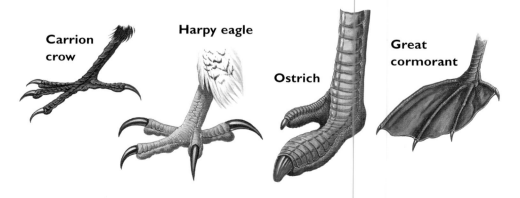

Carrion crow

Harpy eagle

Ostrich

Great cormorant

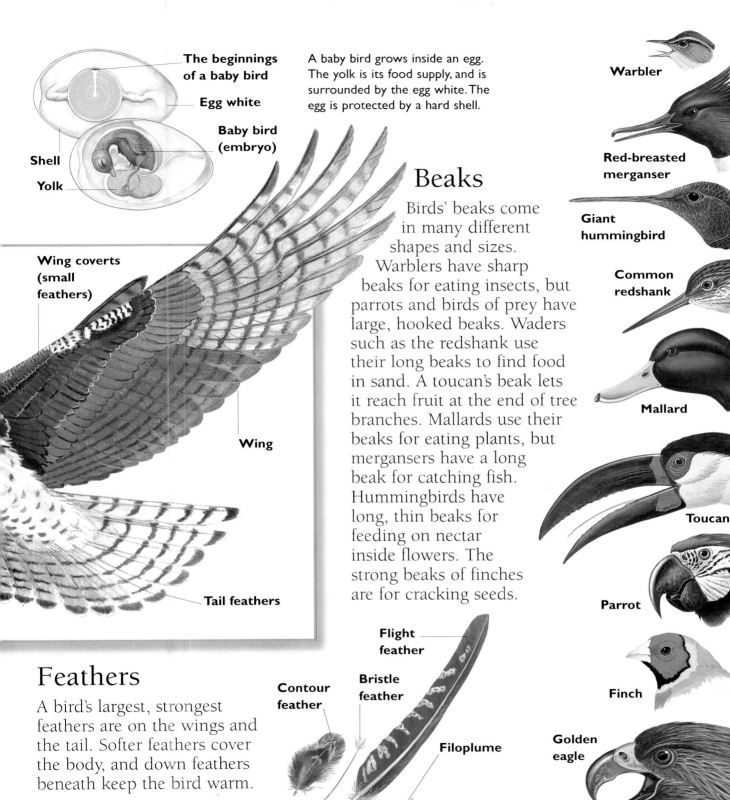

The beginnings of a baby bird

Egg white

Baby bird (embryo)

Shell

Yolk

A baby bird grows inside an egg. The yolk is its food supply, and is surrounded by the egg white. The egg is protected by a hard shell.

Wing coverts (small feathers)

Wing

Tail feathers

Beaks

Birds' beaks come in many different shapes and sizes. Warblers have sharp beaks for eating insects, but parrots and birds of prey have large, hooked beaks. Waders such as the redshank use their long beaks to find food in sand. A toucan's beak lets it reach fruit at the end of tree branches. Mallards use their beaks for eating plants, but mergansers have a long beak for catching fish. Hummingbirds have long, thin beaks for feeding on nectar inside flowers. The strong beaks of finches are for cracking seeds.

Warbler

Red-breasted merganser

Giant hummingbird

Common redshank

Mallard

Toucan

Parrot

Finch

Golden eagle

Feathers

A bird's largest, strongest feathers are on the wings and the tail. Softer feathers cover the body, and down feathers beneath keep the bird warm.

Contour feather

Bristle feather

Flight feather

Filoplume

Owls and birds of prey

Most birds of prey hunt and kill other creatures to eat. They have good eyesight to spot food from the air, strong feet with sharp claws, and a hooked beak for tearing prey apart. Eagles, hawks, and buzzards are all birds of prey. Owls also kill other animals to eat, but, unlike hawks and eagles, they usually hunt at night.

Long-eared owl

13 to 16 inches
North America; Europe; northwestern Africa; Asia

The long tufts on the head of this owl are feathers, not ears. But this bird does have excellent hearing, which helps it catch prey such as voles and mice.

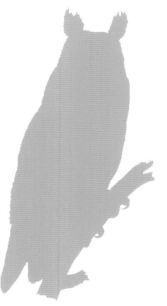

Long-eared owl
A177

Barn owl

16 inches
Worldwide, except temperate Asia, the Arctic, and many Pacific islands

The barn owl is easily recognized by its pale, heart-shaped face. During the day it roosts in a barn or a hole in a tree. At dusk it comes out to hunt for food, usually small creatures such as rats and mice.

Barn owl
A178

Snowy owl

20½ to 25½ inches
Arctic to northern U.S.

The snowy owl hunts both day and night for prey such as mice, hares, and lemmings. The female is bigger than the male and has dark markings on her feathers.

Snowy owl
A179

72

Red kite

24 to 26 inches
Europe; southwestern
Asia; northern Africa

This large bird
of prey has long
wings and a
forked tail. It
hunts in woodlands
and open country and often
hovers as it searches for prey.

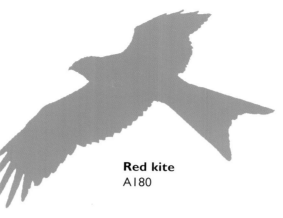

Red kite
A180

Northern goshawk

21 to 26 inches
North America; Europe;
northern Asia

The northern goshawk hunts
creatures such as rabbits and
grouse. It flies through the
forest, weaving in and out of
trees as it chases prey. It kills
its food with its sharp talons.

**Lappet-faced
vulture**
A181

Lappet-faced vulture

3¼ to 3¾ feet
Africa; Israel

Like all vultures, this
bird feeds mostly on
dead animals. It has broad
wings, on which it soars
long distances in search
of food. It has a strong,
hooked beak for tearing
its food apart.

**Northern
goshawk**
A182

Red-tailed hawk

18 to 24 inches
North America, including
the West Indies

This powerful hawk can live
anywhere from forests to deserts.
It hunts birds in the air or swoops
down on prey from a perch.

**Red-tailed
hawk**
A183

Golden eagle
A184

Golden eagle

30 to 40 inches
North America; Europe;
northern Asia; Africa

The golden eagle has a
hooked beak, sharp eyesight,
and strong feet with long,
curved claws. It soars over
land, searching for food.

Osprey

20¾ to 24½ inches
Almost worldwide

This bird of prey flies over
water looking for fish. When
it sees a fish, it plunges
down into the water and
catches its prey in its feet.

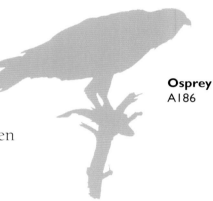

Osprey
A186

Secretary bird

5 feet tall
Africa, south of the Sahara

This long-legged bird eats
prey such as small mammals,
birds, insects, and reptiles.
It kills larger animals by
stomping on them.

Peregrine falcon
A187

Peregrine falcon

16 to 20 inches
Almost worldwide

One of the fastest fliers,
the peregrine preys on other birds. It makes
a high-speed dive toward its prey, often a
pigeon or a dove, and seizes it in midair.

Eurasian kestrel

12¼ to 13¾ inches
Europe; Asia; Africa; western
Canada; Aleutian Islands

The kestrel hunts by
hovering above the ground,
watching for prey. It drops
down and snatches the prey
with its sharp-clawed feet.

Eurasian kestrel
A188

74

Madagascar fish eagle

26¾ to 31 inches
Northwest Madagascar

With less than a hundred pairs left in the world, this fish eagle is one of the rarest birds. It hunts around shallow estuaries and swamps, where it catches fish.

Madagascar fish eagle
❗ A189

King vulture

31 inches
Central and
South America

With its brightly patterned, bare-skinned head, the king vulture is one of the most colorful of all birds of prey. Although it sometimes kills prey for itself, it feeds mostly on dead animals.

Rough-legged hawk

19¾ to 23¾ inches
North America;
northern Europe; Asia

The rough-legged hawk hovers over land as it hunts for prey such as lemmings and voles. It nests in the far north, laying up to four eggs in a nest of twigs made on rock outcrops or along riverbanks.

Rough-legged hawk
A191

King vulture
A190

Bald eagle
A192

Bald eagle

31 to 37 inches
Canada; U.S.

The national bird of the United States, the bald eagle almost died out in the 1960s but has been increasing in numbers since then. The bald eagle feeds mainly on fish.

Birds of the trees and masters of the air

Many birds live in trees. There, among the branches, they can roost, make their nests, and search for food, safe from ground-living hunters. Some birds are more skillful fliers than others. Hummingbirds, for example, are true masters of the air, and swifts are so used to life in the air that they rarely, if ever, walk on land.

Common potoo
A193

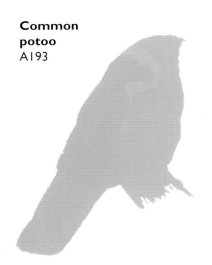

Common potoo

16¼ inches
Central America;
tropical South America

By day, the potoo sits on a broken branch or stump. With its head pointing upward, the potoo looks like part of the tree and is hidden from its enemies.

Crested treeswift

8 inches
Southeast Asia

This swift catches insects in the air to eat. It makes a tiny, cup-shaped nest from thin flakes of bark glued together with spit. There is only room in the nest for a single egg.

Crested treeswift
A194

European nightjar
A195

European nightjar

10¼ inches
Europe; Asia; Africa

The nightjar becomes active at sunset, when it catches moths and other insects in flight. The nightjar's tiny beak opens very wide and is fringed with bristles that help trap its prey.

Ruby-throated hummingbird

3½ inches
Canada; U.S.; winters
in Central America

The ruby-throated
hummingbird uses
its long beak to feed
on nectar deep
inside flowers.

**Ruby-throated
hummingbird**
A196

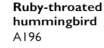

**Common
poorwill**
A197

Common poorwill

7 to 8½ inches
Western North America

Named after its call, which
sounds like "poor will," this
bird hunts insects at dusk and
is rarely seen during the day.

Bank swallow

4¾ to 5 inches
Europe; Asia; North America;
winters in South America,
Africa, and Southeast Asia

The bank swallow nests in
a burrow that it digs into a
sandbank near water.

**Bank
swallow**
A199

**Barn
swallow**
A198

Barn swallow

6¾ to 7¾ inches
Almost worldwide

The barn swallow nests in
barns or other buildings,
where it makes a nest of
mud and grass on a wall.
It feeds on flying insects.

White-throated swift

6 to 7 inches
Western U.S.; Central America

Swifts are fast fliers that spend most of
their lives in the air. Their legs and feet
are tiny and are rarely used for walking.

**White-
throated
swift**
A200

77

Resplendent quetzal

15 to 16 inches;
tail feathers 24 inches
Central America

The male has long tail feathers that wave and flutter as he flies and displays to the female.

Resplendent quetzal
A203

Victoria crowned pigeon

23 to 29 inches
New Guinea

The Victoria crowned pigeon is the world's largest pigeon. This beautiful bird is now rare because of hunting.

Rufous-tailed jacamar
A201

Rufous-tailed jacamar

9 to 11 inches
Central America;
South America

The jacamar darts out from its perch to catch flying insects in midair.

Victoria crowned pigeon
A204

Hoopoe

11 inches
Europe; Asia; Africa

This striking bird has a large crest that can be raised or lowered. It makes a nest in a hole in a tree, a wall, or in the ground. The female lays up to nine eggs.

Hoopoe
A202

Blue-crowned motmot
A205

Blue-crowned motmot

15 to 16 inches
Central America;
South America

This bird's tail swings from side to side as it sits on a branch, watching for prey.

Pileated woodpecker

15 to 19 inches
U.S.

This woodpecker clings to a tree trunk and hammers the bark with its strong beak to find food.

Double-toothed barbet
A206

Double-toothed barbet

9 inches
Central Africa

This barbet has two sharp, toothlike edges on its beak. It feeds on fruit and termites.

Pileated woodpecker
A208

Belted kingfisher

11 to 14 inches
North America

The kingfisher watches for prey from a tree overhanging a river or stream, then dives down to seize a fish or frog from the water.

Belted kingfisher
A207

Bee-eater
A210

Eurasian collared dove
A209

Eurasian collared dove

12 inches
Parts of Europe and Asia; introduced into the Bahamas and mainland North America

This dove lives close to people in towns and the countryside. It feeds on seeds, berries, and scraps put out by people.

Bee-eater

11 inches
Europe; Asia; Africa

The bee-eater eats bees, as its name suggests. It rubs its prey on a branch before eating it in order to remove the poison.

Temperate birds
Forage

Find all the stickers of birds that live in mild, temperate climates on page 158. Stick them on this page and arrange them on the branches of the trees.

80

❗ Ribbon-tailed astrapia

Birds of paradise

Birds of paradise are among the most beautiful and spectacular of all birds. Some are mainly black, with patches of shiny feathers, while others are colored brilliant blue, red, and yellow. Only the males have the colorful head and tail feathers—the females are very different, with dull, usually brownish plumage. Most live in the rain forests of New Guinea. Fruit is their main food, but they also catch insects, spiders, frogs, and lizards.

Ribbon-tailed astrapia

The male has ribbonlike tail feathers, which are nearly 3 feet long.

King of Saxony bird of paradise

King of Saxony bird of paradise

The male of this species has two long plumes on its head. He uses them in a courtship display to the female.

An upside-down display

The male blue bird of paradise hangs upside down from a branch to attract females. He swings to and fro while making a loud call.

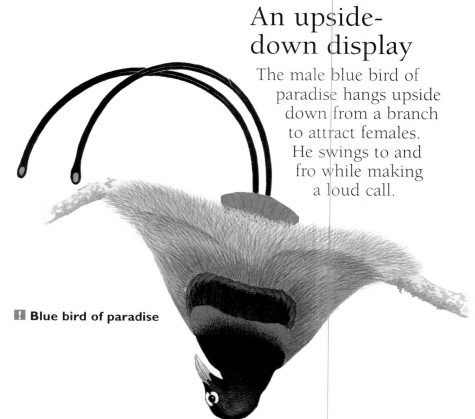

❗ Blue bird of paradise

A group display

Most male birds of paradise display alone, but the raggianas gather in groups. Each tries to outdo the others in showing off his plumage, with much wing flapping and excited calling.

Raggianas bird of paradise

Tail plumes

The male Wilson's bird of paradise has two coiled tail feathers. They are held at right angles to the body when the bird displays.

Wilson's bird of paradise

The striking colors and long tail plumes of the greater bird of paradise are a spectacular sight as it perches on a branch in the rain forest.

Royal flycatcher

6½ inches
Southern Mexico; West Indies;
Central and South America

This flycatcher has an amazing crest that usually lies flat, but can be opened like a fan during its display. Like all flycatchers, it feeds on insects that it snaps up while flying.

**Rufous
hornero**
A211

**Royal
flycatcher**
A212

Rufous hornero

7½ to 8 inches
Eastern South America

The rufous hornero searches for food on the ground, digging out earthworms and insects with its sharp beak. It makes a dome-shaped nest of mud and straw, and the female lays up to five eggs.

**Eastern
kingbird**
A214

Superb lyrebird
A213

Superb lyrebird

Male 31½ to 37½ inches;
female 29½ to 33 inches
Australia

Only the male lyrebird has a long, lyre-shaped tail. In the breeding season, he displays to the female by spreading his tail feathers and dancing.

Eastern kingbird

8 to 9 inches
North America; winters
in South America

This noisy bird attacks anything that enters its territory, particularly larger birds. It eats insects, which it catches in the air or on the ground, or scoops out of water. It also eats berries.

Garnet pitta

6 inches
Malaysia; Sumatra; Borneo

Both male and female garnet pittas have bright feathers, but young birds are a dull brown. This bird spends much of its time on the ground, catching ants, beetles, and other insects.

Wire-tailed manakin
A215

Wire-tailed manakin

4½ inches
South America

Only the male manakin has brightly colored plumage, but both male and female have long, wiry tail feathers.

Torrent tyrannulet

4 inches
Central and South America

This bird lives by fast-flowing streams. It often gets wet as it takes insects from rocks surrounded by foaming water.

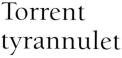

Torrent tyrannulet
A217

Garnet pitta
A216

Andean cock-of-the-rock
A218

Andean cock-of-the-rock

15 inches
Northwestern South America

In the breeding season, groups of male cocks-of-the-rock perform displays to attract the females.

Long-billed woodcreeper
A219

Long-billed woodcreeper

14 inches, including bill
Northern South America

Using its long beak, this woodcreeper searches rain forest plants for insects and spiders to eat. It uses its stiff tail for support as it climbs trees.

85

Tropical birds play page

You can find all the stickers of tropical birds on page 158. Stick them on this page to create your own tropical scene.

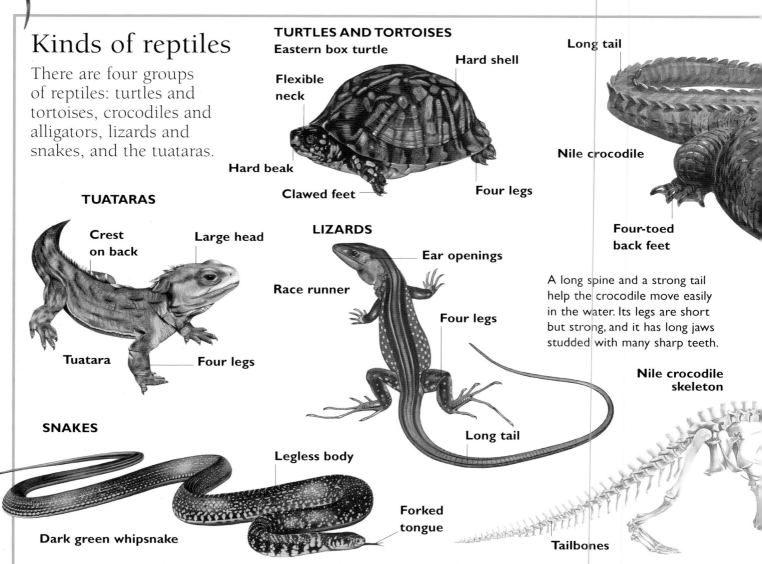

What is a reptile?

Reptiles are vertebrates—like mammals and birds, they have a backbone made up of small bones called vertebrae. Their bodies are covered in tough, waterproof scales. Most reptiles live on land, but some live in water.

Green iguana

Reptiles are cold-blooded and need the sun's warmth to be active. As a result, most live in warm climates. They usually switch between basking in the sun to gain heat and moving to shade or into burrows to cool down.

Kinds of reptiles

There are four groups of reptiles: turtles and tortoises, crocodiles and alligators, lizards and snakes, and the tuataras.

TURTLES AND TORTOISES

Eastern box turtle

Flexible neck

Hard shell

Hard beak

Clawed feet

Four legs

TUATARAS

Crest on back

Large head

Tuatara

Four legs

LIZARDS

Race runner

Ear openings

Four legs

Long tail

SNAKES

Dark green whipsnake

Legless body

Forked tongue

Long tail

Nile crocodile

Four-toed back feet

A long spine and a strong tail help the crocodile move easily in the water. Its legs are short but strong, and it has long jaws studded with many sharp teeth.

Nile crocodile skeleton

Tailbones

Egg-laying reptiles

Most reptiles lay eggs, but some give birth to live young. The egg is protected by a tough shell. The baby grows inside the egg until it is ready to hatch out.

Python incubating eggs

Turtle laying eggs

Yolk sac

Leathery shell

Embryo reptile

Most reptiles, such as turtles, simply lay their eggs in a safe place and leave them to hatch by themselves. Some snakes, such as pythons, curl around their eggs to keep them warm.

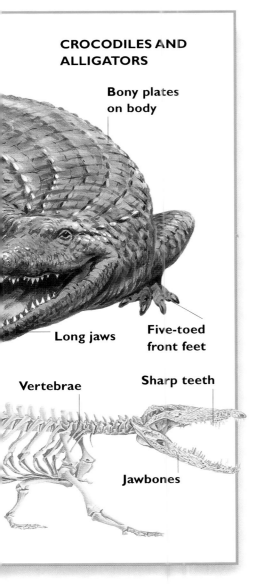

CROCODILES AND ALLIGATORS

Bony plates on body

Long jaws

Five-toed front feet

Vertebrae

Sharp teeth

Jawbones

Prehistoric reptiles

Dinosaurs were prehistoric reptiles, and lived on the earth for 160 million years. They had scaly skin and laid eggs.

Lambeosaurus with young

Crocodiles and alligators

There are thirteen species of crocodiles, seven species of alligators and caimans, and two species of gavials. They are all large, armored reptiles that live both on land and in water. They are covered by hard scales for protection and are fierce hunters of other animals. Males and females look similar, but males tend to grow larger. Crocodiles and alligators have a pair of large teeth near the front of their lower jaw for grasping prey.

Gavial

Up to 18 feet
Southern Asia from Myanmar to Nepal and northern India

The gavial has long jaws containing about 100 small teeth—ideal for catching fish and frogs. This crocodile moves awkwardly on land and rarely leaves the water except to nest. The female lays 35 to 60 eggs in a pit that she digs with her back feet. She stays nearby for up to three months until the eggs hatch.

Gavial
❗ A221

American alligator
A220

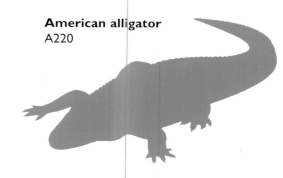

American alligator

Up to 23 feet
Southeastern U.S.

At one time American alligators became very rare because hunters killed so many for their skins. The species is now protected, and it has become more common. The female lays about 50 eggs in a mound of leaves, and guards the nest until the eggs hatch. The young stay with their mother for up to two years.

Mugger crocodile

Up to 13 feet
Bangladesh; India; Iran;
Nepal; Pakistan; Sri Lanka

The mugger is a powerful
crocodile with a broad
snout. It can kill
mammals as large
as deer and buffalo,
but also eats
frogs, snakes,
and turtles.

Spectacled caiman
A222

Mugger crocodile
A223

Spectacled caiman

5 to 6½ feet
Mexico to northern
South America

This caiman lives in any
watery habitat, including
those made by humans, such
as reservoirs and ponds. Like
many crocodiles, this caiman
has become rare, as so many
have been hunted and killed
for their skins.

West African dwarf crocodile
A224

West African dwarf crocodile

Up to 5 feet
Western Africa,
south of the Sahara

This crocodile has become
rare in recent years because
of changes to the rivers and
lakes where it lives and
because of hunting. It is
active at night, when it feeds
on crabs, frogs, and fish.

Saltwater crocodile

Up to 27 feet
Southern India; Indonesia;
southern Australia

This is one of the largest
and most dangerous of all crocodiles. It has
been known to attack humans. It lives mostly
in the sea, catching fish, but it also kills land
animals such as monkeys, cattle, and buffalo.

Saltwater crocodile
A225

Nile crocodiles

Unlike most reptiles, the female Nile crocodile is a good parent. After mating, she digs a pit near the river and lays 16 to 80 eggs. She covers the nest with soil, then both parents guard it for six to eight weeks until the eggs hatch. The mother may care for her young until they are six months old.

The crocodile's nest

The nest is made near water on a sandy beach or riverbank and is 7 to 17 inches deep. Once she has dug the nest burrow, the female lays her eggs inside.

Beginning life

When they are ready to hatch, the young crocodiles listen for any movements on the earth above them. When they hear their mother's footsteps, they make a chirping sound. The mother uncovers the nest and each baby uses its sharp egg tooth to chip its way out of its shell. The mother may help pull the babies free. Once the young crocodiles are out of the eggs, they must find shelter from the many predators waiting to catch them. The mother picks the babies up, a few at a time, and carries them in her mouth to a safe nursery site. She releases her babies in a quiet pool and defends them fiercely.

The Nile crocodile does not live only in the Nile River. It is found in rivers and lakes all over tropical and southern Africa. Adults can measure more than 16 feet long.

Fierce hunter

The Nile crocodile lurks in the water, often with only its eyes and nostrils showing. It drags prey into the water and drowns it.

Turtles and tortoises

There are about 270 kinds of turtles and tortoises. They usually have a hard shell to protect their soft body. Most turtles and tortoises can pull their head inside the shell for protection. They have hard beaks instead of teeth for tearing off pieces of food. Turtles and tortoises lay eggs. Most bury them in sand or earth and leave the young to make their own way out.

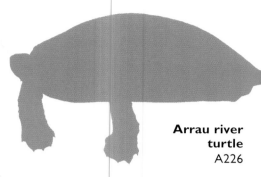

Arrau river turtle
A226

Arrau river turtle

34¼ inches
Northern South America

This is the largest of the turtles known as sidenecks. These turtles pull their head into the shell sideways.

River terrapin
⚠ A227

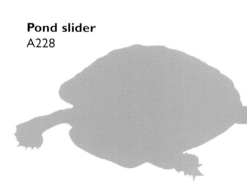

River terrapin

22¾ inches
Southeast Asia

A large, plant-eating turtle, the river terrapin lives in salt water and rivers. It lays its eggs in sandbanks.

Pond slider

5 to 11¾ inches
U.S.; Central America to Brazil

The pond slider rarely moves far from water. It often basks on floating logs. Young pond sliders feed mainly on insects and tadpoles, but as they grow they also eat plants.

Pond slider
A228

Wood turtle

5 to 9 inches
Eastern Canada, northeastern to midwestern U.S.

This rough-shelled turtle stays near water but spends most of its life on land.

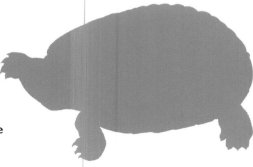

Wood turtle
⚠ A229

Galápagos giant tortoise

Up to 4 feet
Galápagos Islands

This huge tortoise may weigh more than 475 pounds, and males are usually larger than females. It lives on land and feeds on almost any plants it can find.

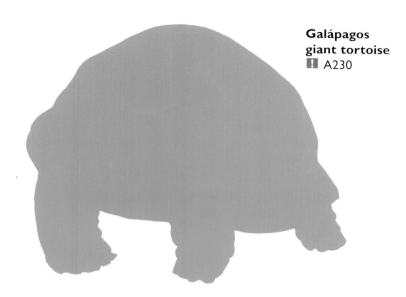

Galápagos giant tortoise
A230

Pancake tortoise
A231

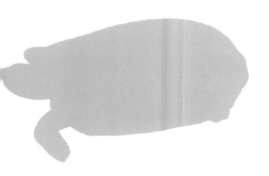

Pancake tortoise

6 inches
Africa

If in danger, this tortoise crawls into a hole and puffs up its body so that it gets stuck and is hard to pull out.

Spur-thighed tortoise

6 inches
Northern Africa; southeastern and southwestern Europe; southwestern Asia

Millions of these tortoises have been taken from the wild and sold as pets, and the species is now rare.

Spur-thighed tortoise
A233

Schweigger's hingeback tortoise

13 inches
Western and central Africa

The hingeback gets its name from its unusual shell—a hinge allows the rear of the

Schweigger's hingeback tortoise
A232

shell to be lowered to protect the animal if it is attacked by an enemy.

Matamata

16¼ inches
Northern South America

The unusual shape of this turtle keeps it well hidden as it lies among dead leaves on the riverbed. Fleshy flaps at the sides of its head wave in the water and may attract small fish.

Matamata
A234

Murray River turtle

11¾ inches
Southeastern Australia

Newly hatched Murray River turtles have almost circular shells. As they grow, the shell becomes wider at the back. Adult shells are oval.

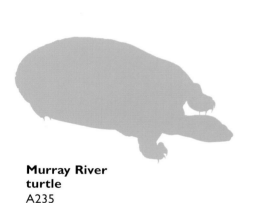

Murray River turtle
A235

Hawksbill

30 to 36 inches
Tropical Atlantic, Pacific, and Indian Oceans; Caribbean

Hawksbills, which are sea turtles, have long been hunted for their beautiful shells as well as for their eggs. There are now strict controls on hunting, but it is still very rare.

Hawksbill
⚠ A236

Leatherback

Leatherback
⚠ A237

...opical Atlantic, Pacific, and Indian Oceans, b... migrates to temperate waters

The world's largest sea turtle, the leatherback weighs about 800 pounds. Its shell is not covered with hard plates but is made of a thick, leathery skin.

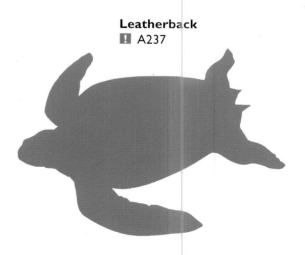

Loggerhead turtle

30 to 80 inches
Temperate and tropical Pacific, Atlantic, and Indian Oceans; Mediterranean Sea

Loggerheads return to breed on the same beaches where they hatched. Females lay about 100 eggs in the sand.

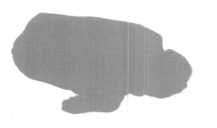

Loggerhead turtle
❗ A238

Common musk turtle

3 to 5 inches
U.S.

Also known as the stinkpot, this turtle produces a strong-smelling fluid if attacked.

Common musk turtle
A239

Atlantic green turtle

3¼ to 4 feet
Tropical Atlantic, Pacific, and Indian Oceans

This turtle spends most of its life in the sea eating seaweed. It may travel a long way to lay its eggs on the beach where it was born.

Atlantic green turtle
❗ A240

Spiny softshell

Spiny softshell
A241

5 to 18 inches
North America

Softshell turtles can move fast on land and in water but spend most of their lives in water. The spiny softshell feeds on insects, crayfish, and some fish and plants.

Alligator snapping turtle

Alligator snapping turtle
❗ A242

14 to 26 inches
Central U.S.

This turtle can weigh up to 200 pounds. It has a pink, fleshy flap on its lower jaw.
Any passing small creatures that come to try this "bait" are quickly swallowed.

97

Beach play page

You can find all the stickers of reptiles that live in the sea or on beaches on page 159. Stick them on this page to create your own beach scene.

Lizards

Lizards are the largest group of reptiles. They range from tiny geckos only 3 inches long to huge Komodo dragons up to 10 feet long. Most lizards have four legs, but some are legless. Many lizards lay eggs in a hole or under a rock, but some keep their eggs in their body until the babies inside are well developed. The babies are born when the eggs hatch, but some lizard babies are born live.

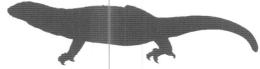

Chuckwalla

11 to 16½ inches
Southwestern U.S.; Mexico

This plump lizard lies among rocks at night and comes out in the morning to warm its body by basking in the sun. A plant-eater, it spends the day feeding on leaves, buds, and flowers.

Leaf-tailed gecko

8 inches
Madagascar

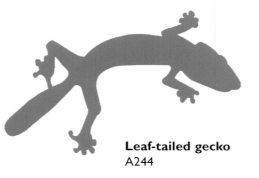

Leaf-tailed gecko
A244

The spotted pattern on the body of this gecko blends well with tree bark, hiding the lizard against a tree trunk. The gecko is usually active at night, catching insects to eat. After eating, it cleans its whole body with its tongue.

Web-footed gecko
A245

Web-footed gecko

5 inches
Southwestern Africa

This desert-living gecko has webbed feet, which helps it run over soft sand. It burrows into the sand to

hide from enemies or the burning sun. It sits in its burrow waiting to pounce on insects such as termites.

Arabian toad-headed agamid

Up to 5 inches
Southwestern Asia

This lizard digs tunnels for shelter or buries itself in the desert sand. If alarmed, it warns off the enemy by lifting its tail high, then rolling and unrolling it.

Tuatara

Up to 25½ inches
New Zealand

There are only two living species of tuataras. Experts who have studied ancient fossils believe that tuataras are similar to lizards that lived 130 million years ago.

Green iguana
A246

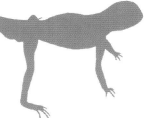

Arabian toad-headed agamid
A247

Rhinoceros iguana

Up to 4 feet
West Indies

This iguana is named for the pointed scales on the male's snout, which look like the horns of a rhinoceros.

Tuatara
A249

Marine iguana

4 to 5 feet
Galápagos Islands

Green iguana

3¼ to 6½ feet
Central America; South America; West Indies; introduced into the U.S.

A tree-living lizard, the iguana also swims well. It defends itself fiercely with its teeth and claws if attacked.

Rhinoceros iguana
A248

Marine iguana
A250

The marine iguana is the only lizard that spends most of its life in the sea. It swims using its powerful tail.

101

Desert night lizard

3¾ to 5 inches
Southwestern U.S.

This lizard lives among desert plants and feeds on termites, ants, flies, and beetles. It does not lay eggs but gives birth to one to three live young, which develop inside the female's body.

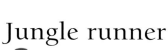

Desert night lizard
A252

Green anole

4¾ to 7¾ inches
Southeastern U.S.

The male anole has a flap of pink skin on his throat that he fans in a display to mark his territory.

Green anole
A251

Jungle runner

2½ to 9½ inches
Central America, South America east of the Andes; introduced into Florida

This very active lizard hunts on the ground. The female is smaller than the male, and her body is marked with stripes instead of spots.

Jungle runner
A254

Gila monster
⚠ A253

Gila monster

17¾ to 24 inches
Southwestern U.S.; Mexico

This is one of only two poisonous lizards. As it bites its prey, poison flows into the wound. The Gila eats birds, mammals, and eggs.

Western blue-tongued skink

17¾ inches
Southern Australia

This plump-bodied lizard has a large head. It scurries around searching for insects, snails, and berries. The female gives birth to up to 25 live young.

Western blue-tongued skink
A255

Komodo dragon

10 feet
Komodo and some neighboring islands in the Lesser Sunda Islands

The Komodo dragon is large enough to kill deer, wild boar, and pigs.

Komodo dragon
A256

Slow worm
A257

Slow worm

13¾ to 21¼ inches
Parts of Europe and western Asia; northwestern Africa

The slow worm looks like a snake, but is actually a legless lizard. It sleeps under rocks or logs. The female gives birth to live young.

Frilled lizard

26 to 36 inches
Australia; New Guinea

This lizard has a collar of skin that lies in folds around its neck. If the lizard is disturbed, its collar stands up like a frill, making it look bigger.

Frilled lizard
A258

Great Plains skink

6½ to 13¾ inches
Central U.S.; Mexico

This lizard is unusual because the female guards her eggs carefully while they incubate and protects them from predators.

Transvaal snake lizard

15¾ inches
South Africa

With snakelike movements of its long body and tail, this lizard moves through the grass searching for insects.

Transvaal snake lizard
A259

Great Plains skink
A260

103

Snakes

Snakes are slender, legless creatures that range in size from 4 inches to 30 feet. Despite having no legs, snakes can move quickly across the ground or even up tree trunks. A snake's eyes are always open and watching for movement. Some snakes, such as boas, squeeze their prey to death, while others, such as vipers, have a poisonous bite.

Western blind snake
A261

Western blind snake

7 to 15 inches
Southwestern U.S.

The western blind snake has a blunt head and tail. It lives underground where there is sandy or gravelly soil.

Boa constrictor

Up to 18½ feet
Central and South America

The boa constrictor kills prey, such as birds and mammals, by wrapping the victim in the strong coils of its body and squeezing it to death. The boa spends most of its life on the ground, but also climbs trees.

Indian python
A262

Anaconda

30 feet
South America,
east of the Andes

The anaconda lives in slow-moving water. When an animal comes to drink, the snake seizes its prey with its mouth, then coils around it and squeezes.

Indian python

16½ to 20 feet
India; southeast Asia; Indonesia

This python is one of the largest snakes. It basks in the sun by day or rests in a cave. At night it hunts for birds, small deer, and boar, or waits near a water hole where animals are sure to come.

Boa constrictor
A263

Anaconda
A264

Gopher snake

4 to 8¼ feet
Southwestern Canada;
U.S.; Mexico

This large snake is a good climber and burrower. Usually active in the daytime, it hunts rats and mice as well as rabbits and birds. If alarmed, it flattens its head, hisses loudly, and shakes its tail to warn the enemy before attacking it.

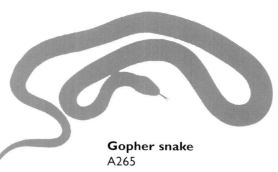

Gopher snake
A265

Eastern hognose snake

20 to 45 inches
Eastern U.S.

If in danger, the hognose snake gives a warning display, puffing itself up and hissing loudly. If this does not scare off its enemy, the snake plays dead, lying still with its tongue hanging out.

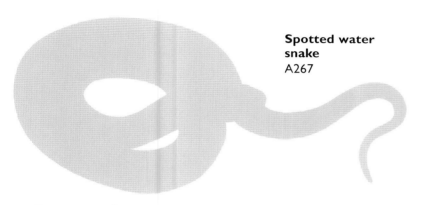

Spotted water snake
A267

Eastern hognose snake
A266

Spotted water snake

11¾ to 39 inches
Australia

This snake is able to move quickly both in water and on land. It preys on creatures such as fish and frogs. Its eyes and nostrils are on the top of its head. It is mildly poisonous.

Grass snake

Up to 6½ feet
Europe; northwestern
Africa; western Asia

The grass snake is one of the most common snakes in Europe. It is a good swimmer and hunts fish and frogs in rivers, and mice on land.

Grass snake
A268

Scarlet kingsnake
A269

Scarlet kingsnake

14 to 27 inches
Southeastern Canada;
U.S.; Mexico

This kingsnake spends much of its life hidden under logs or tree stumps.

Sidewinder

17 to 32¼ inches
Southwestern U.S.;
Mexico

The poisonous sidewinder moves sideways across the sand as it hunts for prey.

Sidewinder
A272

Paradise tree snake

Up to 4 feet
Philippines to Indonesia

Also known as the flying snake, the paradise tree snake lives in trees. It can flatten its body and glide 65 feet or more from tree to tree in the rain forest.

Paradise tree snake
A271

Eastern coral snake
A273

Banded sea snake
A270

Banded sea snake

6½ feet
Coastal areas of Indian and Pacific Oceans

This snake lives in the sea and can stay underwater for up to two hours. Like all sea snakes, it eats fish and has a poisonous bite.

Eastern coral snake

22 to 48 inches
Southeastern U.S.;
northeastern Mexico

The colorful markings of the coral snake warn enemies that it is poisonous. It hunts lizards and small snakes, which it kills with its poisonous bite.

Indian cobra

6 to 7¼ feet
India; central and southeastern Asia; Philippines

This large, very poisonous cobra feeds on mice, lizards, and frogs. It can attack or defend itself from a distance by spitting out jets of poison. This can cause severe pain if it reaches the eyes of mammals.

To threaten its enemies, the cobra rears up the front of its body.

Indian cobra
A275

Eastern diamondback rattlesnake
A274

Gaboon viper

4 to 6½ feet
Western Africa, south of the Sahara

The highly poisonous Gaboon viper has fangs that are up to 2 inches long. It hunts at night, preying on mice, frogs, and birds.

Egg-eating snake

29½ inches
Africa, south and east of the Sahara

This snake's mouth can stretch wide enough to swallow an egg much larger than its head. The whole egg passes into the throat, where the snake crushes the shell before swallowing the contents.

Eastern diamondback rattlesnake

 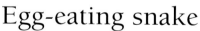

3¼ to 7¾ feet
Eastern to midwestern U.S.

Like all rattlesnakes, the diamondback makes a rattling sound using a series of hard, hollow rings of skin at the end of its tail. This is the most dangerous snake in the United States.

Gaboon viper
A276

Egg-eating snake
A277

Desert play page

You can find all the stickers of reptiles that live in the desert on page 159. Stick them on this page to create your own desert scene.

What is an amphibian?

Amphibians are cold-blooded animals, which means that they cannot control their own body temperature. Some bask in the sun to warm up or enter water to cool down. An amphibian's skin is not scaly, and must be kept moist.

Taking off

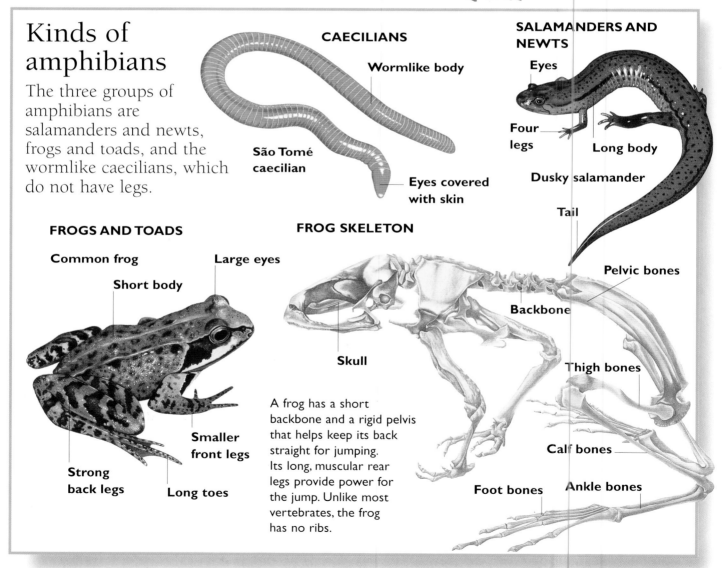

Kinds of amphibians

The three groups of amphibians are salamanders and newts, frogs and toads, and the wormlike caecilians, which do not have legs.

CAECILIANS

Wormlike body

São Tomé caecilian

Eyes covered with skin

SALAMANDERS AND NEWTS

Eyes

Four legs

Long body

Dusky salamander

Tail

FROGS AND TOADS

Common frog

Short body

Large eyes

Smaller front legs

Strong back legs

Long toes

FROG SKELETON

Skull

Backbone

Pelvic bones

Thigh bones

Calf bones

Foot bones

Ankle bones

A frog has a short backbone and a rigid pelvis that helps keep its back straight for jumping. Its long, muscular rear legs provide power for the jump. Unlike most vertebrates, the frog has no ribs.

110

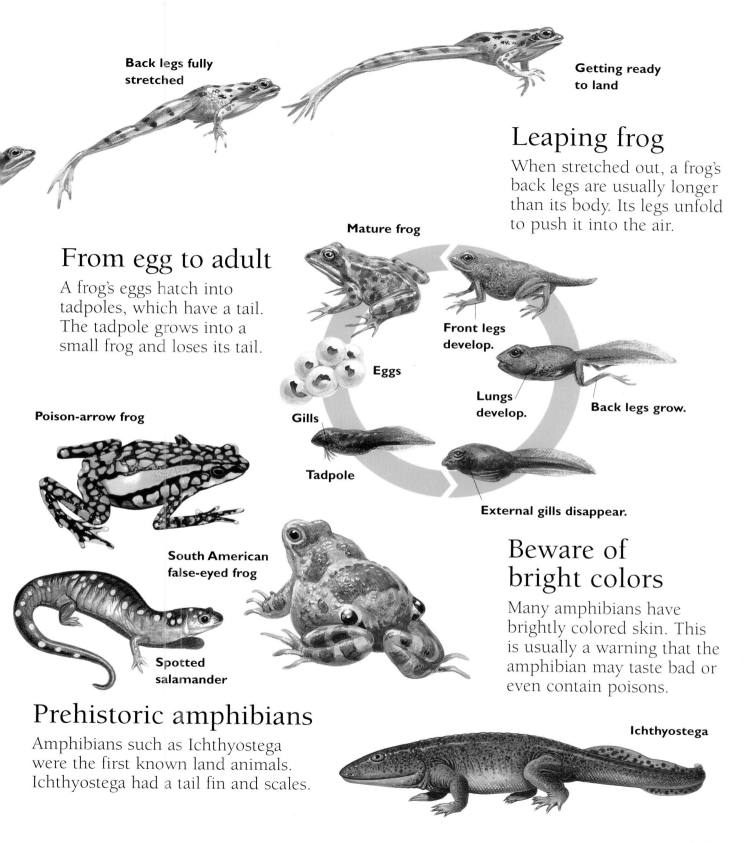

Back legs fully stretched

Getting ready to land

Leaping frog

When stretched out, a frog's back legs are usually longer than its body. Its legs unfold to push it into the air.

From egg to adult

A frog's eggs hatch into tadpoles, which have a tail. The tadpole grows into a small frog and loses its tail.

Mature frog

Front legs develop.

Eggs

Lungs develop.

Back legs grow.

Gills

Tadpole

External gills disappear.

Poison-arrow frog

South American false-eyed frog

Spotted salamander

Beware of bright colors

Many amphibians have brightly colored skin. This is usually a warning that the amphibian may taste bad or even contain poisons.

Prehistoric amphibians

Amphibians such as Ichthyostega were the first known land animals. Ichthyostega had a tail fin and scales.

Ichthyostega

111

Salamanders and newts

There are about 350 species of salamanders and newts. Sirens, amphiumas, olms, and mud puppies are all long-bodied amphibians with small, almost useless legs. The lungless salamanders are the largest group. There are about 53 species of newts. There are water- and land-living newts, but most stay near water.

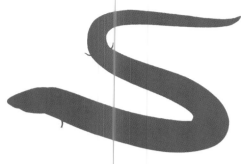

Two-toed amphiuma
A278

California slender salamander

3 to 5½ inches
Western U.S.: Oregon, California

California slender salamander
A279

True to its name, this salamander has a long, slim body and tail. Its legs and feet are tiny, and it moves by wriggling its body rather than by using its legs.

Two-toed amphiuma

17¾ to 45½ inches
Southeastern U.S.

The amphiuma lives only in water. It has a long body and tiny legs that are useless for walking. It hunts at night.

Olm

7¾ to 11¾ inches
Balkan Peninsula; Italy

Olm
⚠ A280

This strange-looking salamander has a long body, a flattened tail, and small, weak legs. It is almost blind and lives in darkness in the streams and lakes of caves.

Red salamander
A281

Red salamander

3¾ to 7 inches
Eastern U.S.

The brilliantly colored red salamander has a stout body and a short tail and legs. It lives mostly on land but usually stays near water.

Texas blind salamander

3½ to 5¼ inches
U.S.: southern Texas

This blind salamander lives in water in underground caves in total darkness. Its blood shows through its colorless skin, making it look pink. It eats cave-dwelling invertebrates.

Texas blind salamander
A283

Greater siren

19¾ to 38½ inches
Southeastern U.S.

The siren has a long, eel-like body and tiny front legs with four toes on each foot. It has no back legs and swims by fishlike movements of its body.

Greater siren
A285

Mud puppy
A282

Mud puppy

7¾ to 17 inches
Southern Canada; U.S.

The mud puppy spends all its life in water. It hunts worms, crayfish, and insects at night. The female lays up to 190 eggs, each stuck to a log or rock.

Spotted salamander
A284

Spotted salamander

6 to 9½ inches
Southeastern Canada; eastern U.S.

Spotted salamanders spend most of their time alone and out of sight, burrowing through damp soil. But every spring they gather in large numbers around pools to mate and lay their eggs in the water.

Tiger salamander

6 to 15¾ inches
North America

The tiger salamander is the world's largest land-living salamander. It has a stout body, broad head, and small eyes. It lives near water and often hides among leaves or in a burrow.

Tiger salamander
A286

Pacific giant salamander
A287

Pacific giant salamander

2¼ to 11¼ inches
Northwestern North America

Most salamanders are silent, but this species makes a low-pitched cry. They live on land and are active at night.

Fire salamander
A288

Fire salamander

7¼ to 11 inches
Parts of Europe; southwestern Asia; northwestern Africa

Bright markings warn predators that this salamander's body is covered with an unpleasant-tasting slime.

Axolotl

Up to 11½ inches
Lake Xochimilco in Mexico

This salamander is now rare because so many have been caught for the pet trade. Many are also eaten by fish in the lake where they live.

Axolotl
⚠ A289

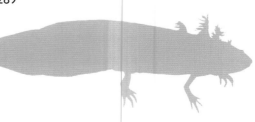

Warty newt
A290

Warty newt

5½ to 7 inches
Parts of Europe; central Asia

The male of this large, rough-skinned newt grows a jagged crest on his back in the breeding season. Warty newts feed on small invertebrates, fish, and other amphibians.

South American caecilian

13¾ inches
South America, east
of the Andes

Caecilians are not salamanders but belong to a separate group of blind amphibians. They burrow into the ground. This caecilian has a short, thick body.

South American caecilian
A291

Eastern newt
A292

Hellbender

12 to 29¼ inches
U.S.

Despite its name, this large salamander is a harmless creature that hides under rocks in the water during the day. At night it hunts crayfish, snails, and worms, which it finds by smell and touch rather than by sight. The female lays up to 500 eggs on a streambed.

Hellbender
A293

Eastern newt

2½ to 5½ inches
Eastern North America

The young of this newt, which are called efts, leave the water when they are a few months old. They spend up to three years on land before returning to water.

Frogs and toads

There are more than 3,500 species of frogs and toads. An adult frog or toad has long back legs, webbed toes, and no tail. The skin is either smooth or warty. Like all amphibians, frogs and toads are sometimes at home on land and sometimes in freshwater. Frogs and toads lay eggs that hatch into tailed, swimming young known as tadpoles. As the tadpoles grow, they develop legs, and they finally lose their tails and become frogs or toads.

African clawed toad

2½ to 5 inches
Africa, south of the Sahara

This toad moves as fast in the water as any fish and can even swim backward. It uses its claws to dig in the mud around pools and streams for food. It eats any creatures it can find, even its own tadpoles.

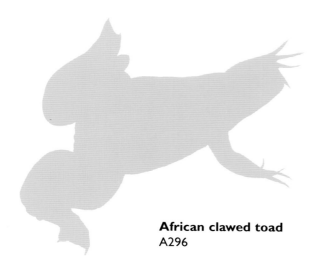

African clawed toad
A296

Glass frog
A294

Glass frog

Up to 1 inch
Central America and northern South America

This delicate little frog lives in small trees and bushes, usually near running water. It has sticky pads on its toes, which help it grip when climbing.

Natal ghost frog
A295

Natal ghost frog

Up to 2 inches
Northeastern South Africa

This frog lives in fast-flowing mountain streams. The female lays her eggs in a pool. When the tadpoles move into the streams, they hold on to stones with their mouths to avoid being swept away.

Cane toad

4 to 9½ inches
U.S.: southern Texas; Central and South America; Africa; southern Asia; Australia

One of the largest toads in the world, the cane toad makes a poisonous liquid that can cause irritation or even kill any mammal that tries to eat it.

Cane toad
A297

Midwife toad
A298

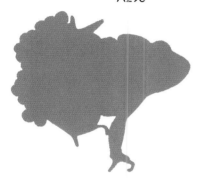

Midwife toad

Up to 2 inches
Western Europe; Morocco

The midwife toad hides by day under logs. Unusually, after the female has laid her eggs, the male looks after them, carrying them around until they hatch.

Oriental fire-bellied toad

2 inches
Siberia; northeastern China; Korea

The brilliantly colored rough skin of the fire-bellied toad gives off a poisonous, milky liquid that irritates the mouth and eyes of any attacker. The female lays her eggs on the undersides of stones in water.

Oriental fire-bellied toad
A299

Western spadefoot

1¼ to 2½ inches
Western U.S.; Mexico

An expert burrower, the western spadefoot toad has a hard spike on each back foot that helps it dig. It spends the day in its burrow and comes out at night to feed.

Western spadefoot
A300

Corroboree frog
■ A301

Corroboree frog

1¼ inches
Australia

This frog lives on land near water and shelters under logs or in a burrow that it digs. The female lays up to a dozen large eggs, which are usually guarded by one parent until they hatch.

Gold frog

Up to ¾ inch
Southeastern Brazil

This tiny frog often lives among dead leaves on the forest floor but may also hide in cracks in trees or rocks in dry weather. It has a bony shield on its back and may use this to block off the entrance of its hiding place.

Marsupial frog

Up to 1½ inches
Northwestern South America

The marsupial frog has an unusual way of caring for its eggs. The female carries her eggs in a skin pouch on her back for a few weeks, until they hatch into tadpoles.

Gold frog
A302

Marsupial frog
A303

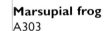

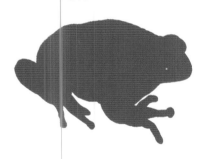

Amazon horned frog
A304

Amazon horned frog

Up to 7¾ inches
Northern and central South America

This horned frog is almost as broad as it is long and has a wide head and large mouth. It has a lump on each upper eyelid. It spends much of its life half-buried in the ground.

118

Darwin's frog

1¼ inches
Southern Chile and
southern Argentina

This frog has unusual
breeding habits. The male
keeps the female's eggs in a
pouch under his chin until
they hatch into tadpoles.

Darwin's frog
A305

Natterjack toad

2¾ to 4 inches
Western and central Europe

The male natterjack has the
loudest call of any European toad.
His croak carries a mile or more.
The natterjack usually lives on land
but is often found near the sea.

**Natterjack
toad**
A307

**European
tree frog**
A306

European tree frog

Up to 2½ inches
Central and southern Europe;
western Asia; northwestern Africa

This smooth-skinned frog
lives in trees. It can change
color very quickly, turning
from bright green in sunlight
to dark gray in shade.

Spring peeper

¾ to 1¼ inches
Southeastern Canada;
eastern U.S.

This agile frog can
climb trees and jump heights
of more than 17 times its
own body length. In the
breeding season, males sit in
trees calling to females with
a high-pitched whistling.

**Spring
peeper**
A308

Arum lily frog

Up to 2¼ inches
Africa, mostly south of the Sahara

This frog changes color as
the light varies. In bright
sun it is light cream,
turning dark brown in
shade. It has sticky
pads on its toes to help
it grip as it climbs.

**Arum lily
frog**
A309

Pond play page

You can find all the stickers of amphibians th~~~~ ~~~~
lakes and ponds on page 160. Stick th~~~~
to create your own pond scene.

Glossary

amphibian A four-legged animal that can live both on land and in water.

bird A two-legged vertebrate that is covered with feathers and has a pair of wings.

bovid A horned, plant-eating animal such as sheep, goats, and cows.

carnivore An animal that eats the flesh of other animals in order to survive.

chewing the cud Bringing back up into the mouth food that has already been eaten and then chewing it for a second time.

colony A group of the same type of animal living together.

extinction The complete dying out of a species.

habitat The natural home of an animal.

herbivore An animal that eats plants.

hibernation Sleeping through almost the entire winter.

hoof The horny covering of the foot on a mammal.

incubate To supply eggs with heat for their development, often by sitting on them.

mammal A warm-blooded animal that usually has hair on its body and feeds its young on milk produced in its own body.

marsupial An animal that continues growing in its mother's stomach pouch after birth.

monotreme An egg-laying, toothless mammal.

nocturnal Active during the night.

predator An animal that hunts and kills other animals for food.

prey An animal hunted by a predator.

primate A mammal with hands and feet.

reptile A cold-blooded animal with lungs and a protective covering of scales. Babies are born from eggs.

rodent A small mammal whose front teeth grow constantly and are gnawed down.

species A term for one type of plant or animal.

temperate Weather that is mild: neither tropical (hot) nor polar (cold).

vertebrate An animal with a backbone. Mammals, birds, reptiles, amphibians, and fish are all vertebrates.

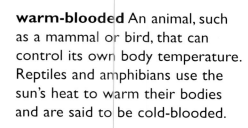

warm-blooded An animal, such as a mammal or bird, that can control its own body temperature. Reptiles and amphibians use the sun's heat to warm their bodies and are said to be cold-blooded.

List of animals

Acknowledgments

ARTWORK CREDITS

Mammals
Graham Allen, John Francis, Elizabeth Gray,
Bernard Robinson, Eric Robson, Simon Turvey,
Dick Twinney, Michael Woods

Birds
Keith Brewer, Hilary Burn, Malcolm Ellis,
Steve Kirk, Colin Newman, Denys Ovenden,
Peter David Scott, Ken Wood, Michael Woods

Reptiles & Amphibians
John Francis, Elizabeth Gray, Steve Kirk, Alan Male,
Colin Newman, Eric Robson, Peter David Scott

Habitat Symbols
Roy Flookes

PHOTOGRAPHIC CREDITS
26–27 Charles O'Rear/ CORBIS; **39** Frank
Schneider Meyer/ Oxford Scientific Films;
40–41 Bruce Heinemann/Getty Images;
45 Martyn Colbeck/ Oxford /Scientific Films;
56–57 Jim Hallett/ Nature Picture Library;
68–69 Global Book Publishing; **80–81** Digital
Vision Ltd; **108–109** Digital Vision Ltd;
120–121 James Randklev/ The Image Bank

Place these stickers on the shapes that match these animals. **Find** them on pages **10–11** and **12–13**.

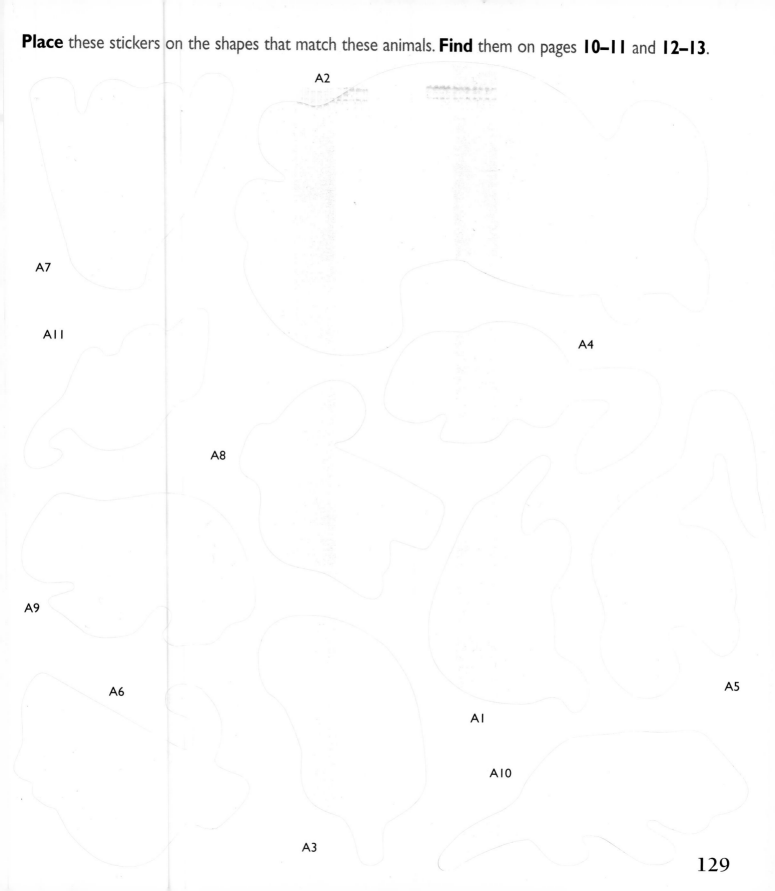

A2

A7

A11

A4

A8

A9

A6

A5

A1

A10

A3

Place these stickers on the shapes that match these animals. **Find** them on pages **12–13** and **14–15**.

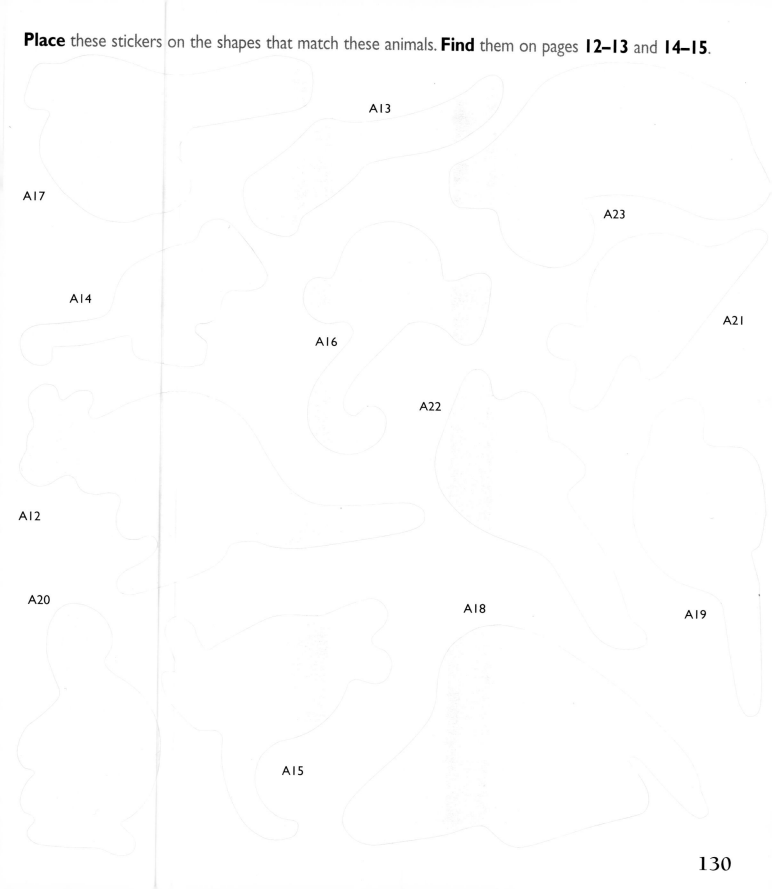

A13

A17

A23

A14

A21

A16

A22

A12

A20

A18

A19

A15

Place these stickers on the shapes that match these animals. **Find** them on pages **16–17** and **18–19**.

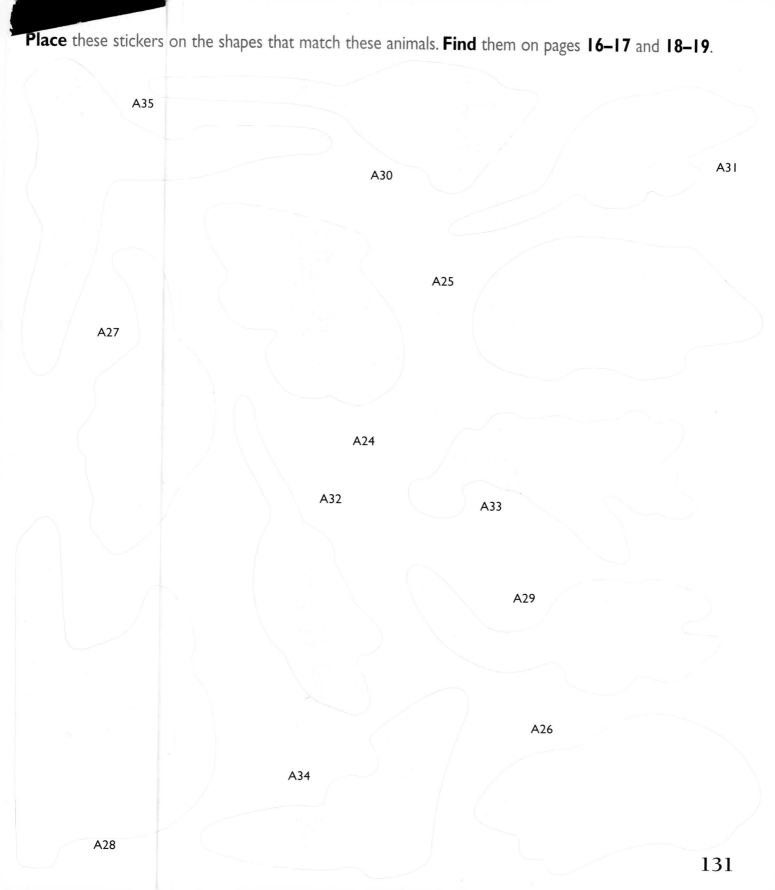

A35

A30

A31

A25

A27

A24

A32

A33

A29

A26

A34

A28

131

Place these stickers on the shapes that match these animals. **Find** them on pages **18–19** and **20–21**.

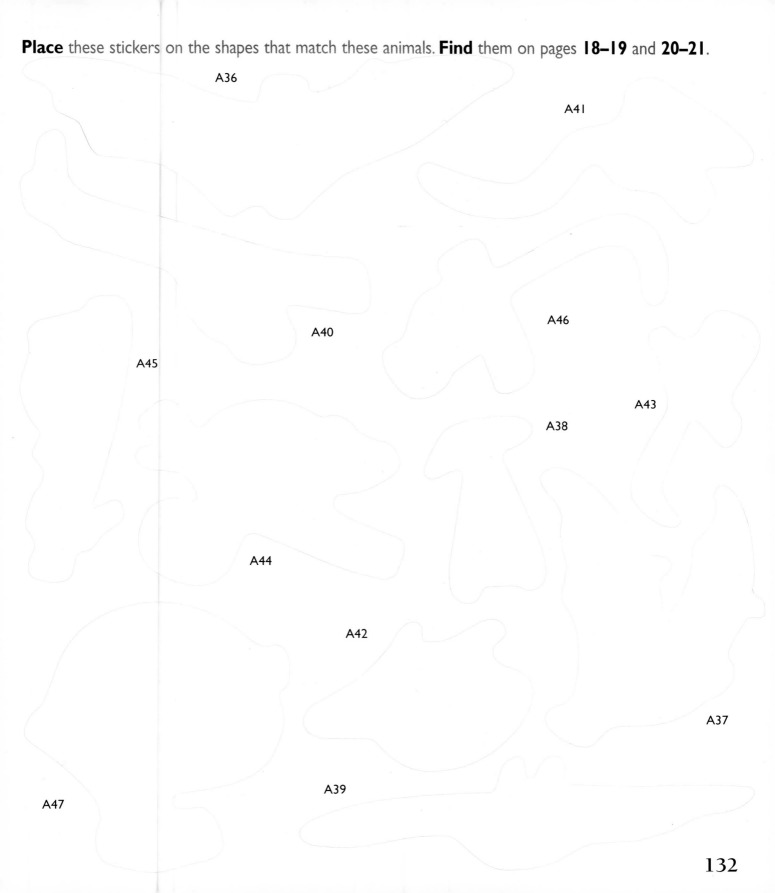

A36

A41

A46

A40

A45

A43

A38

A44

A42

A37

A39

A47

Place these stickers on the shapes that match these animals. **Find** them on pages **22–23**, **24–25**, and **28–29**.

A68

A61

A63

A64

A65

A69

A58

A62

A60

A57

A48

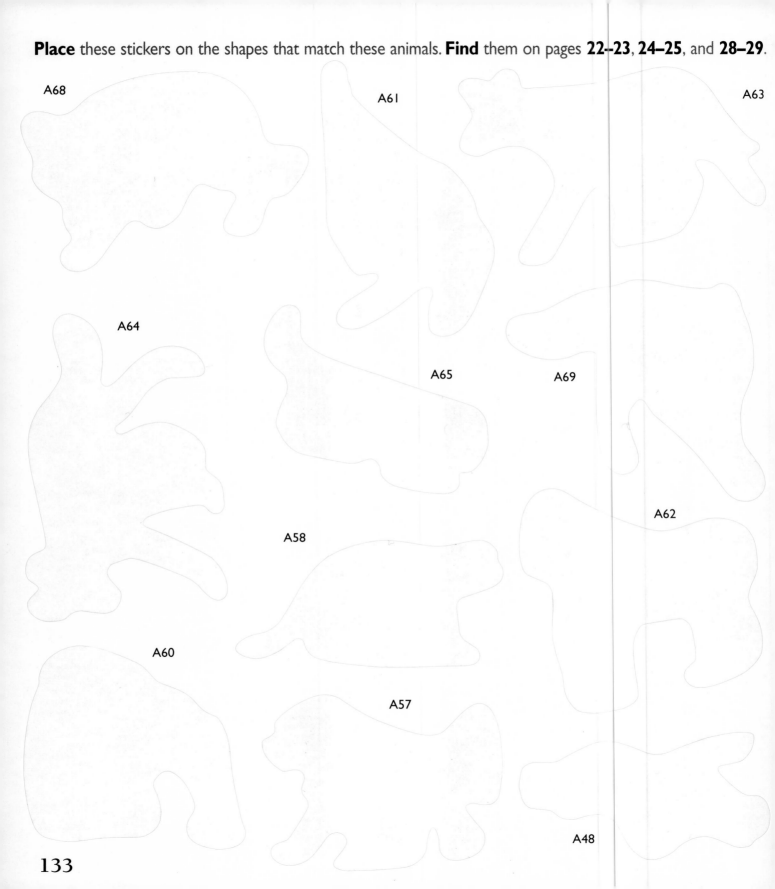

133

Place these stickers on the shapes that match these animals. **Find** them on pages **22–23**, **24–25**, and **28–29**.

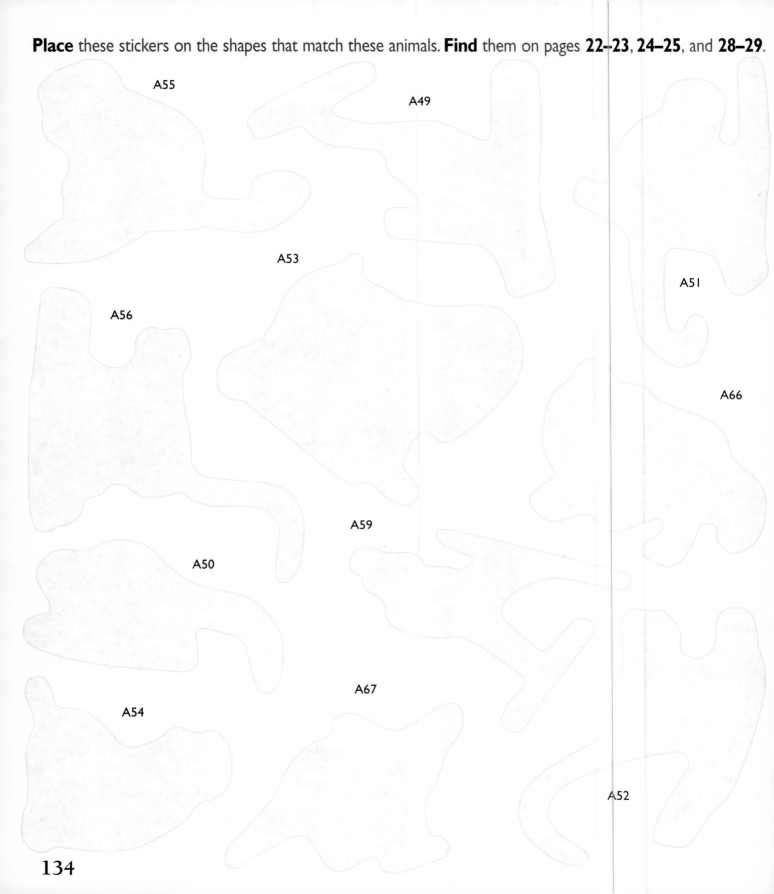

A55

A49

A53

A51

A56

A66

A59

A50

A67

A54

A52

134

Place these stickers on the shapes that match these animals. **Find** them on pages **30–31** and **32–33**.

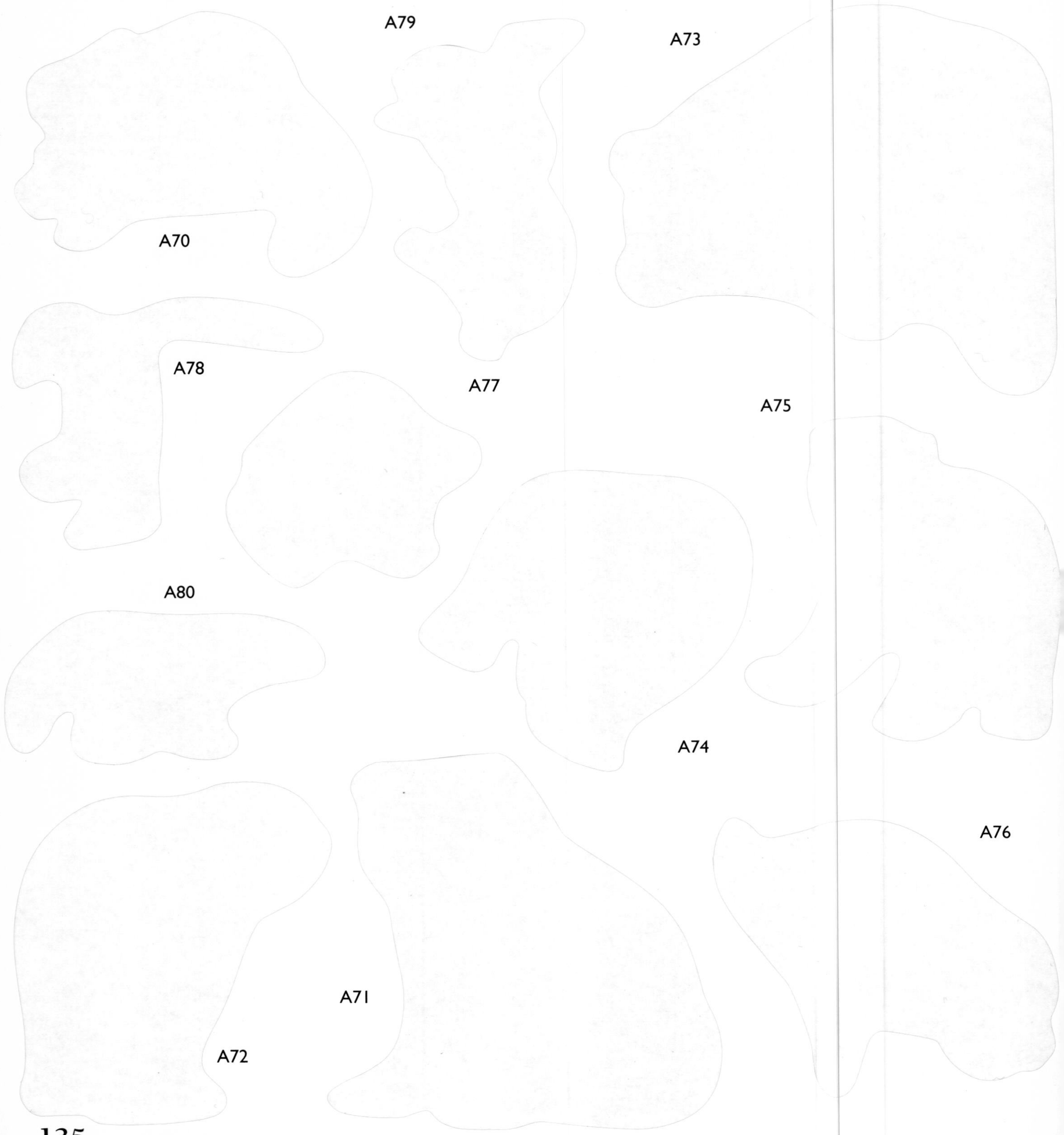

A79

A73

A70

A78

A77

A75

A80

A74

A76

A71

A72

Place these stickers on the shapes that match these animals. **Find** them on pages **32–33** and **34–35**.

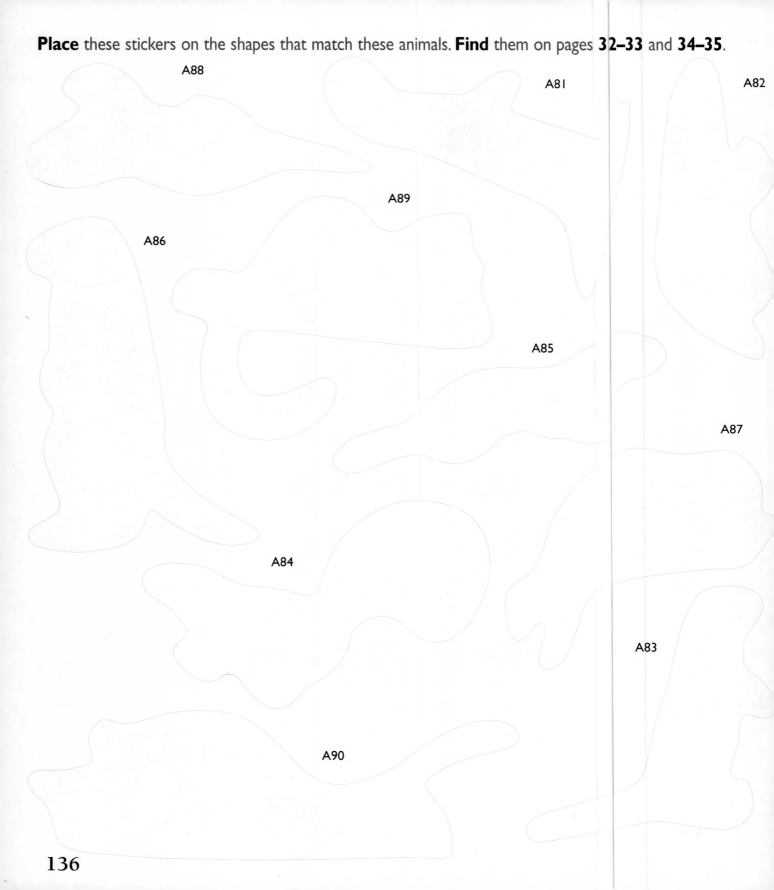

A88

A81

A82

A89

A86

A85

A87

A84

A83

A90

Place these stickers on the shapes that match these animals. **Find** them on pages **36–37** and **42–43**.

A97

A92

A91

A93

A100

A101

A95

A96

A94

A102

A99

A98

137

Place these stickers on the shapes that match these animals. **Find** them on pages **42–43** and **46–47**.

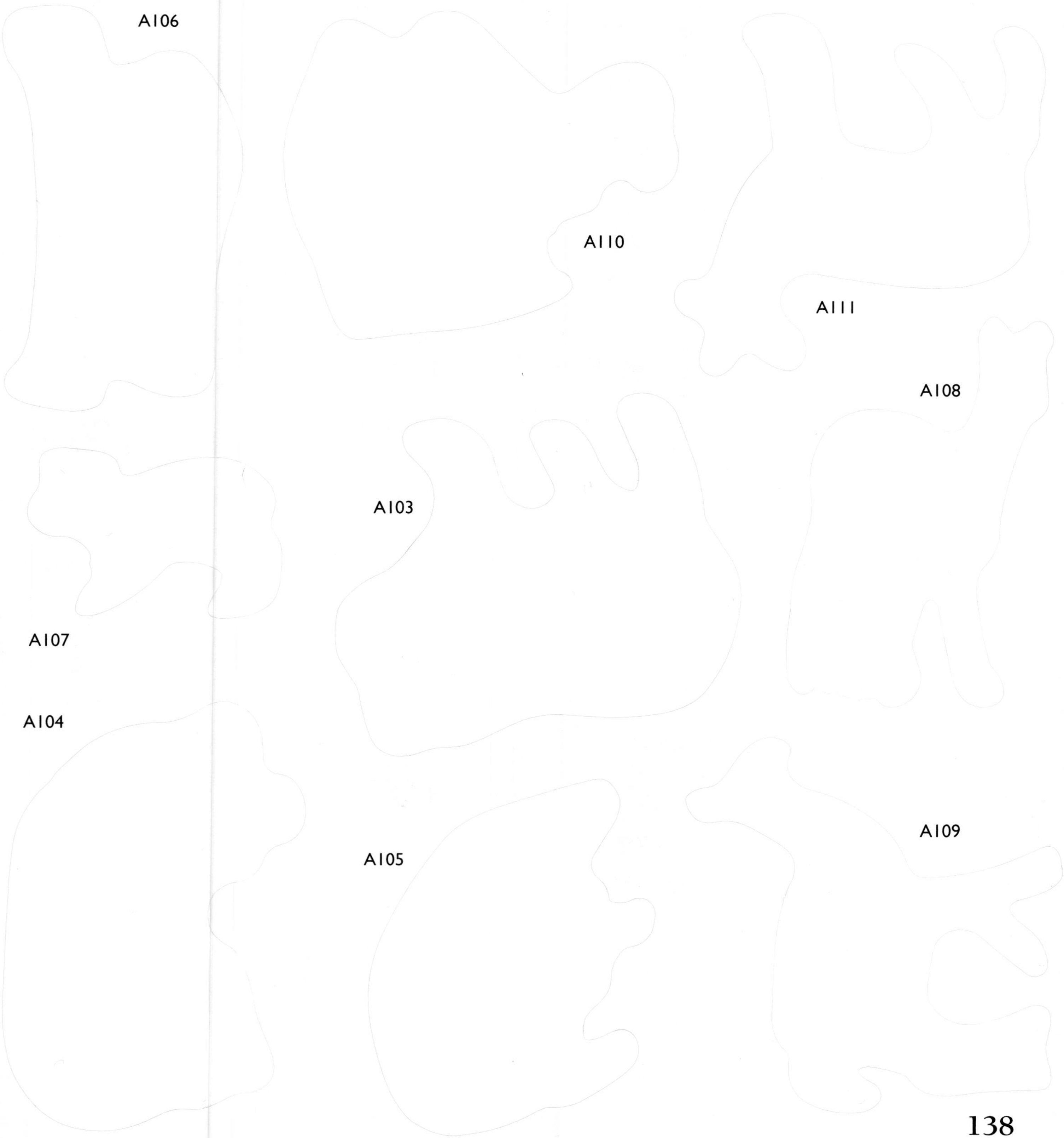

A106

A110

A111

A108

A103

A107

A104

A109

A105

Place these stickers on the shapes that match these animals. **Find** them on pages **48–49** and **50–51**.

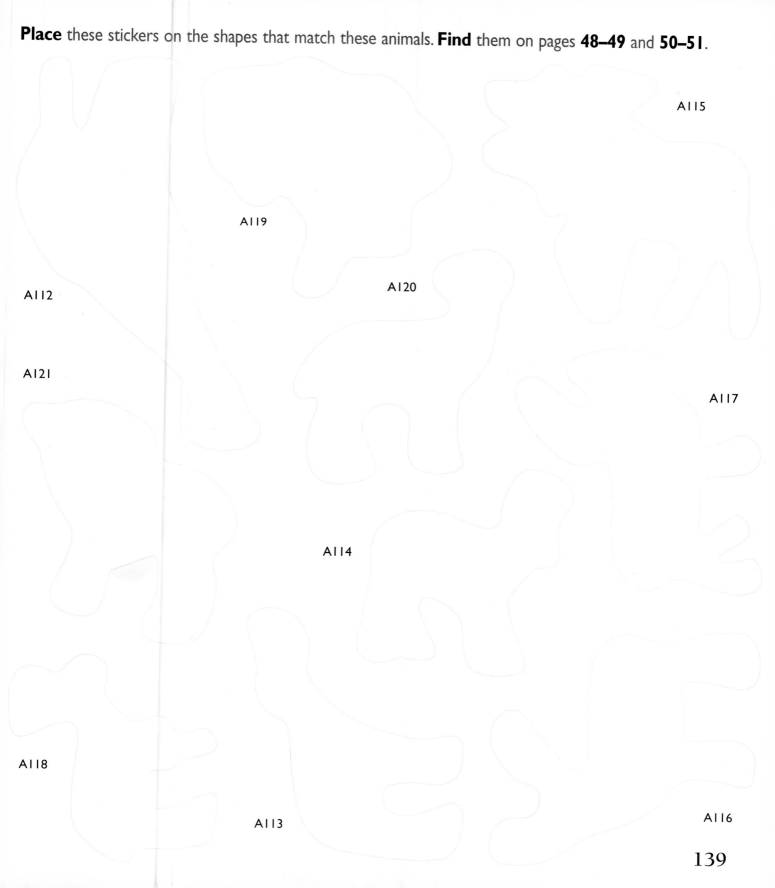

A115

A119

A120

A112

A121

A117

A114

A118

A113

A116

Place these stickers on the shapes that match these animals. **Find** them on pages **50–51** and **52–53**.

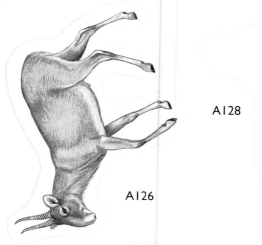

A128

A126

A124

A122

A131

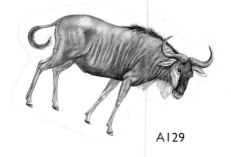

A123

A129

A130

A127

A125

Place these stickers on the shapes that match these animals. **Find** them on pages **54–55** and **58–59**.

A132

A138

A134

A133

A135

A136

A137

A143

A139

A142

Place these stickers on the shapes that match these animals. **Find** them on pages **58–59** and **60–61**.

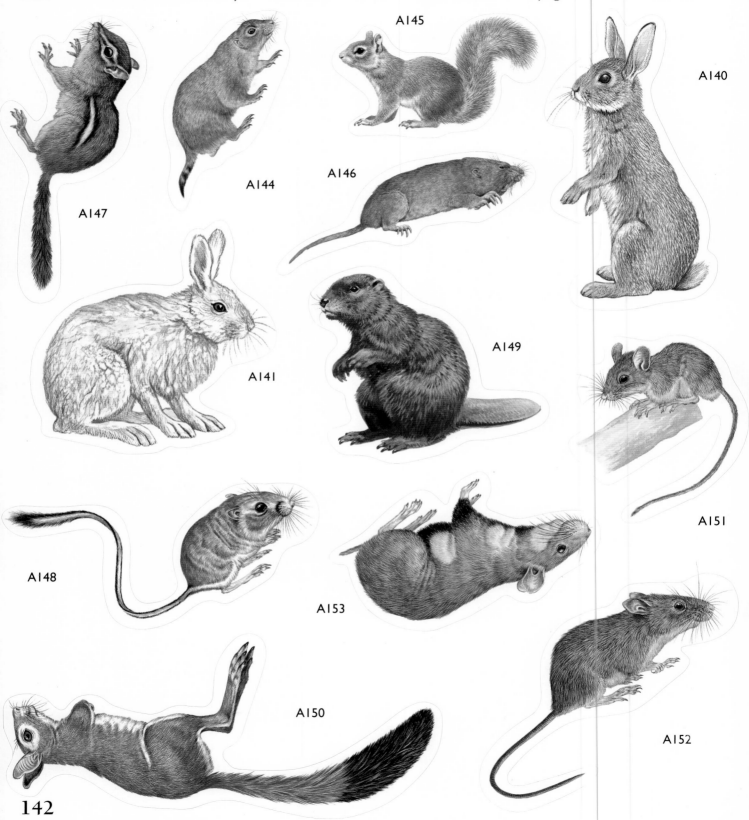

A145

A140

A147

A144

A146

A141

A149

A151

A148

A153

A150

A152

142

Place these stickers on the shapes that match these animals. **Find** them on pages **62–63** and **64–65**.

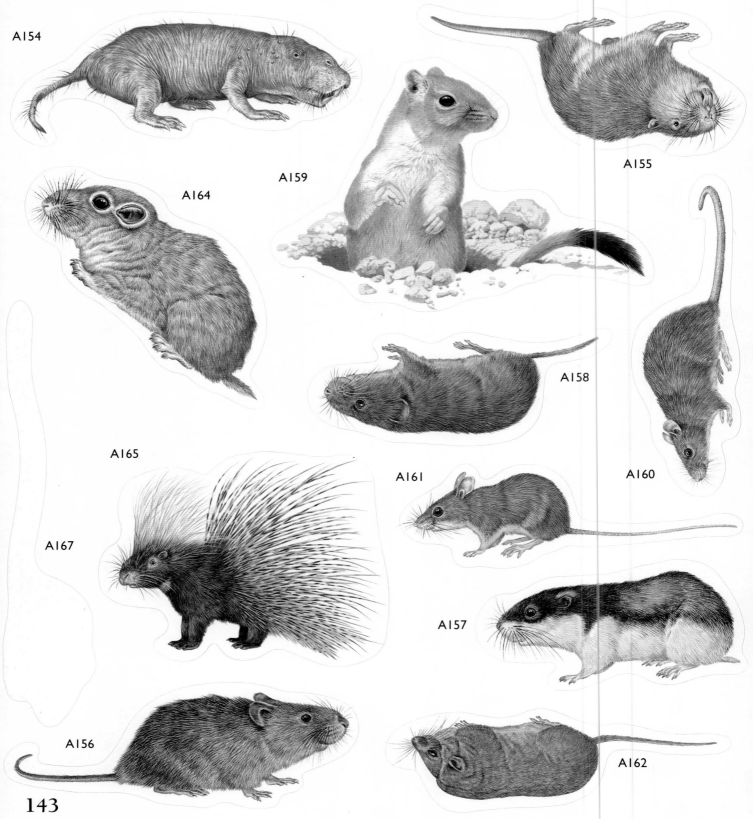

A154

A159

A155

A164

A158

A160

A165

A161

A167

A157

A156

A162

Place these stickers on the shapes that match these animals. **Find** them on pages **64–65** and **66–67**.

A168

A171

A163

A166

A170

A174

A169

A173

A176

A172

A175

Place these stickers on the shapes that match these animals. **Find** them on pages **72–73** and **74–75**.

A177

A182

A187

A178

A184

A185

A183

A188

A181

A186

A179

A180

Place these stickers on the shapes that match these animals. **Find** them on pages **74–75** and **76–77**.

A194

A199

A193

A189

A191

A197

A192

A196

A200

A198

A190

A195

146

Place these stickers on the shapes that match these animals. **Find** them on pages **78–79** and **84–85**.

A203

A207

A202

A206

A201

A208

A204

A205

A210

A217

A212

A209

A214

A211

A218

Place these stickers on the shapes that match these animals. **Find** them on pages **84–85** and **90–91**.

A213

A215

A216

A219

A221

A222

A220

A225

A223

A224

Place these stickers on the shapes that match these animals. **Find** them on pages **94–95** and **96–97**.

A231

A227

A226

A228

A232

A233

A234

A236

A235

A229

A230

149

A248

A246

A250

A247

A245

A241

A237

A244

A238

A242

A239

A243

A249

A240

150

Place these stickers on the shapes that match these animals. **Find** them on pages **102–103** and **104–105**.

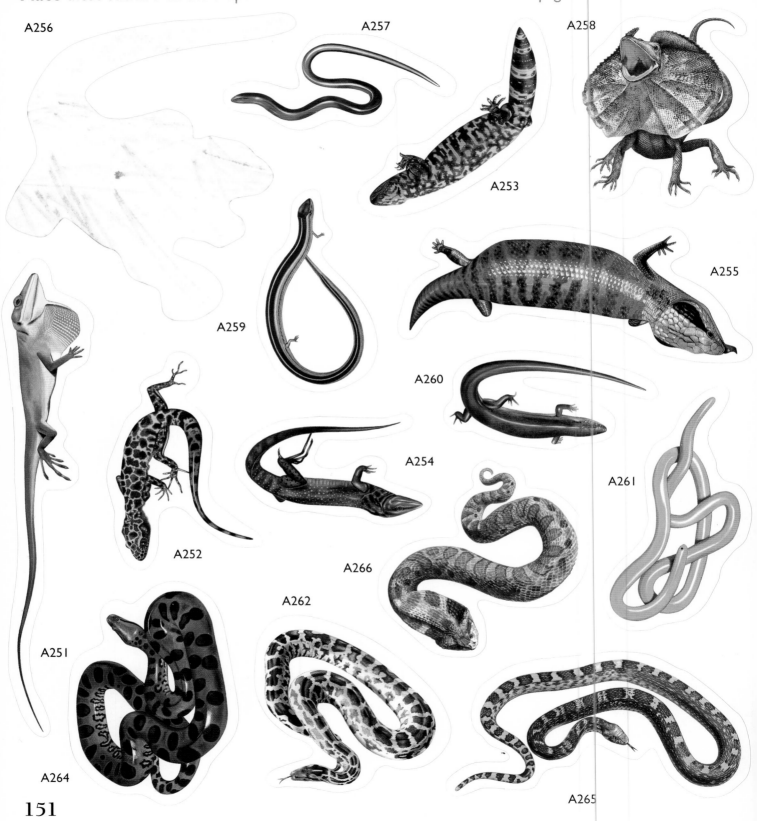

A256

A257

A258

A253

A259

A255

A251

A252

A254

A260

A261

A266

A264

A262

A265

Place these stickers on the shapes that match these animals. **Find** them on pages **104–105**, **106–107**, and **112**.

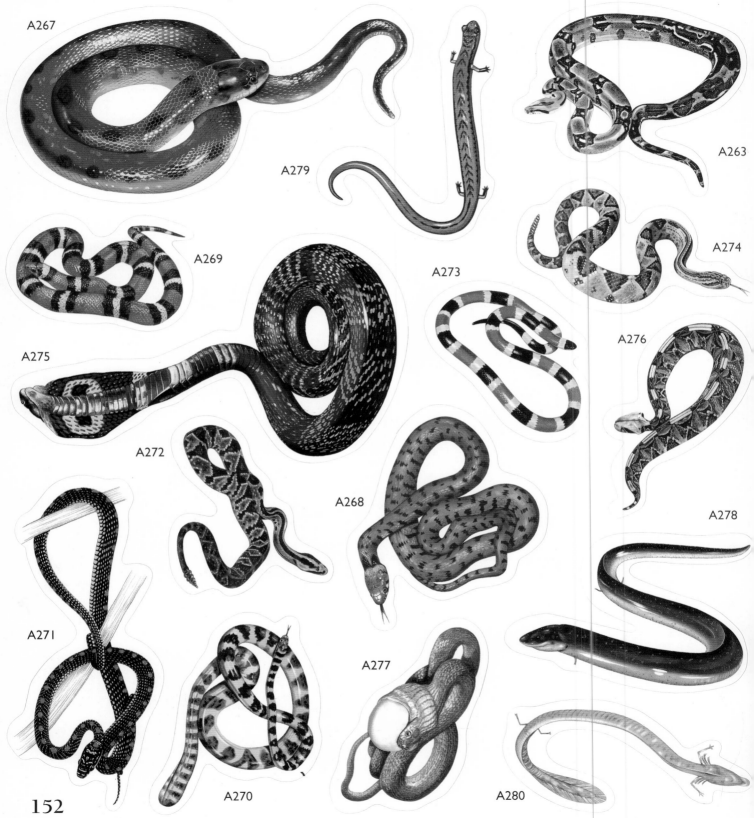

A267

A279

A263

A269

A274

A273

A275

A276

A272

A268

A278

A271

A277

A270

A280

Place these stickers on the shapes that match these animals. **Find** them on pages **113**, **114–115**, and **116**.

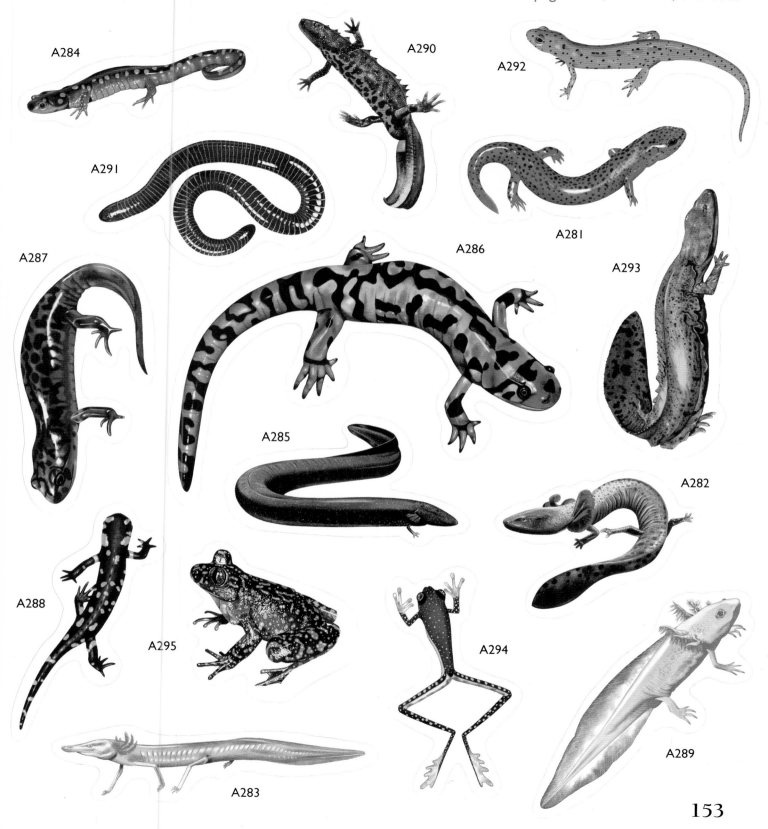

A284

A290

A292

A291

A287

A286

A281

A293

A285

A282

A288

A295

A294

A289

A283

Place these stickers on the shapes that match these animals. **Find** them on pages 116–117 and 118–119.

A303

A301

A306

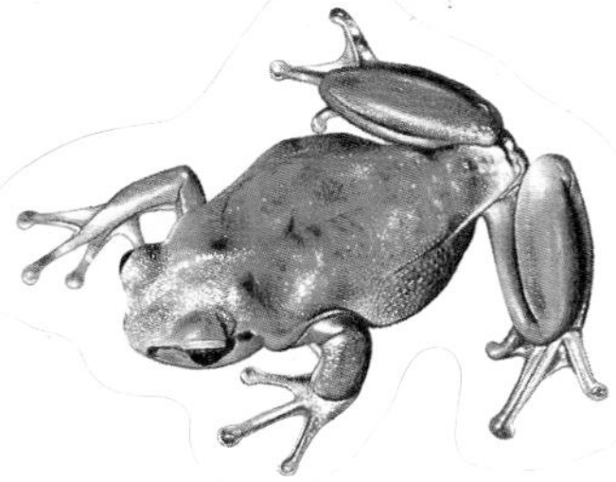

A308

A297

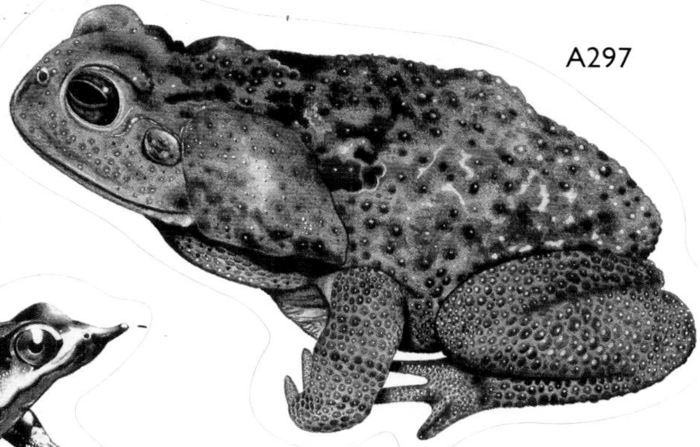

A302

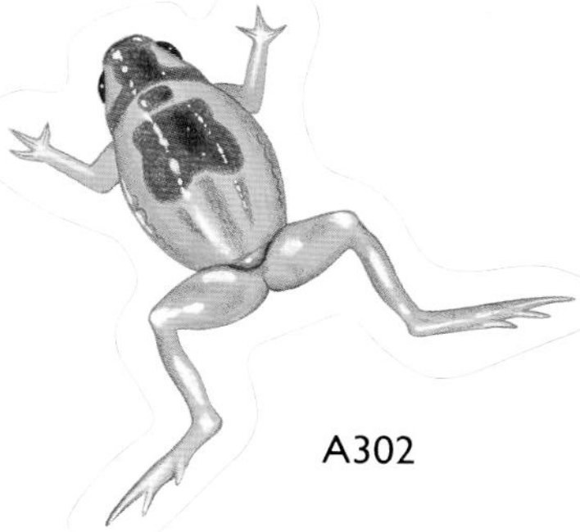

A305

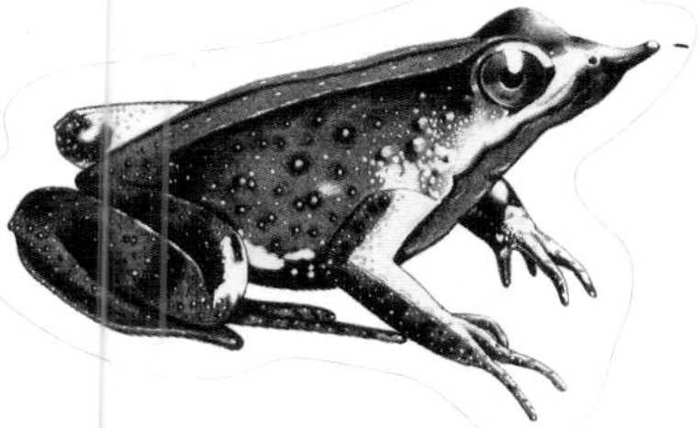

A296

A307

A309

A299

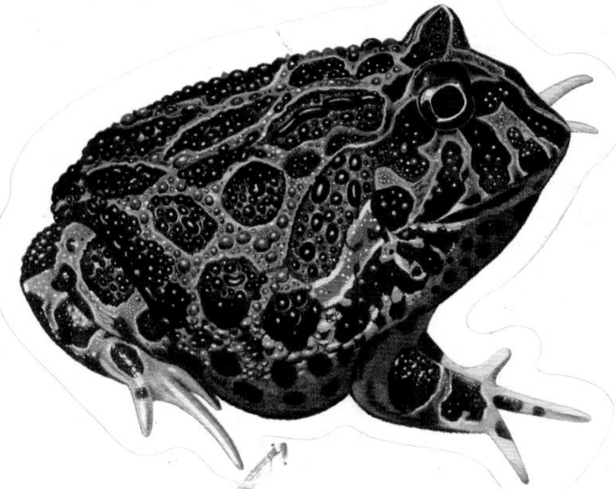

A298

A304

A300

154

Have fun sticking these mammals onto the **Savanna Play Page** on pages **26–27**.

Have fun sticking these mammals onto the
Grassland Play Page on pages **40–41**.

Have fun sticking these mammals onto the
Meadow Play Page on pages **56–57**.

Have fun sticking these mammals onto the **Scrubland Play Page** on pages **68–69**.

Have fun sticking these birds onto the
Temperate Birds Play Page on pages **80–81**.

Have fun sticking these birds onto the
Tropical Birds Play Page on pages **86–87**.

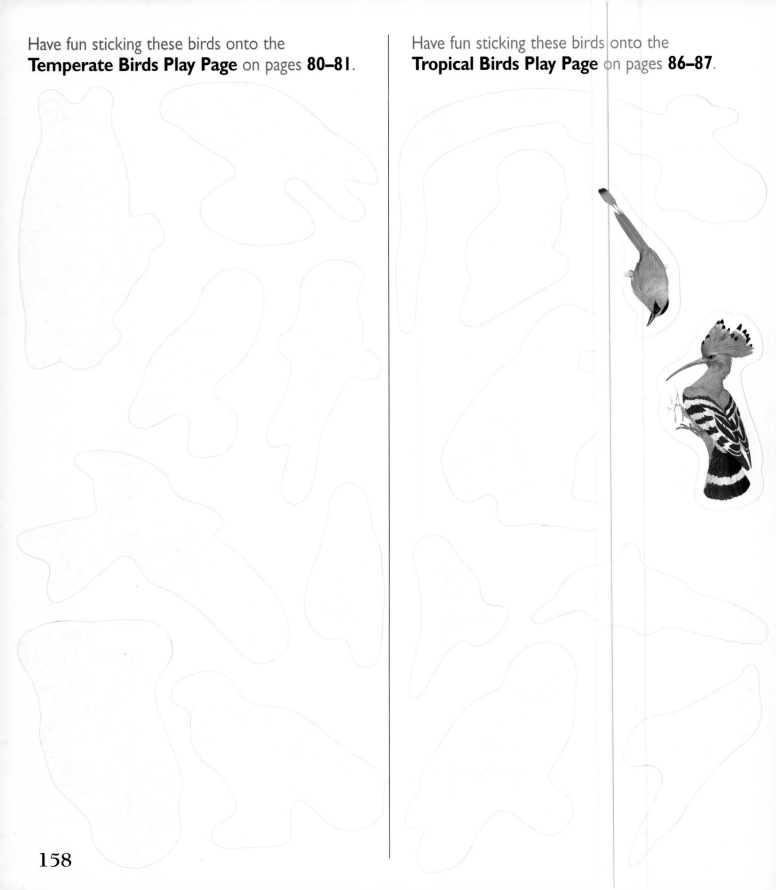

Have fun sticking these reptiles onto the
Beach Play Page on pages **98–99**.

Have fun sticking these reptiles onto the
Desert Play Page on pages **108–109**.

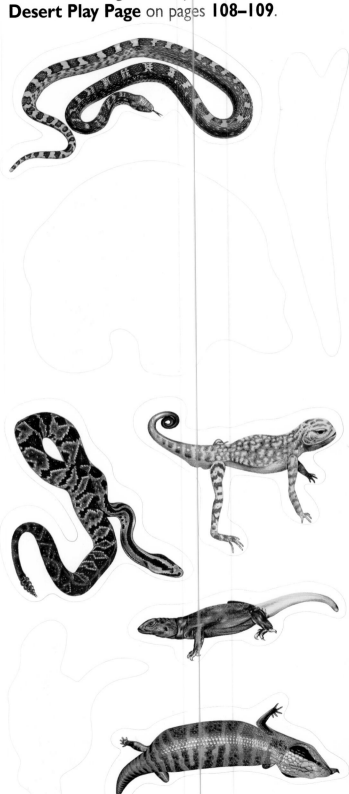

Have fun sticking these amphibians onto the **Pond Play Page** on pages **120–121**.